OUR NEIGHBOURLY GHOSTS

OUR NEIGHBOURLY GHOSTS

Tall and short stories from the West Country

Doreen Evelyn

Illustrations by Sarah Jonas

EX LIBRIS PRESS

First published by
Ex Libris Press
1 The Shambles
Bradford on Avon
Wiltshire

Cover by 46 Design
Typeset in 10 on 12 point Plantin
by Saxon Printing Ltd., Derby
Printed in Great Britain by
A. Wheaton & Co. Ltd., Exeter

ISBN 0 948578 02 5

To Mim, with love

Author's Note

The stories in this book are told in the first person, as they were told to me. Whilst the names of people have been altered, the ghosts remain real. A brief note has been appended to each story to explain its origin and possible historical basis.

CONTENTS

SAIL BOUND

We children never really knew why the family had to move away from London. I can remember overhearing a conversation between Mother and Father which did not make much sense. I was seven at the time, standing patiently by my mother's chair while she untied the rags knotted in my hair and then combed and brushed out my long ringlets. I had to be patient; if I had winced or pulled away I would have been rapped smartly over the knuckles with the hairbrush.

'But, Harold, whatever will we do in Frome? Nobody wants a silversmith there. You can't start all over again and rebuild a business at your time of life. The doctor has warned you repeatedly that your health will suffer.'

'My love, I will abandon my trade,' said Father firmly. 'We will open a general store where we can live on the premises. I won't have to travel to and fro, and the children can help.'

I was puzzled because we already had a shop and a workshop and this lovely house to live in. What were premises?

Now I have hardly any memories of our London home. At the time of the move I thought we were going on holiday and expected daily to be taken back 'home'. Gradually my unhappiness at our protracted stay faded and I began to love our homely cottage with its own well at the bottom of a lovely garden. The shop was in the front of the house where there was a round bay window in which my parents displayed to advantage all sorts of things.

Mother would spend all day Friday making sweets. I was surprised because I had never before seen her work in the kitchen and I was annoyed because we were not allowed to eat the sweets, they were for sale. Mother's toffee became quite famous. During the Sunday service at St John's, the church at the top of the street, the less godly among the children would appropriate half the money given to them for the offertory, wait till the long sermon, then slide along the pews to the side door and scamper to our shop to buy a farthing's worth of sticky toffee. When they had sucked two lumps they headed back to the church to be in their places for the end of the sermon. Mother and Father never knew - they were chapel, and hired an odd job boy to serve on Sundays.

It was on a Sunday that we first heard the strange knockings. I was still in bed. The cottage had two bedrooms on the first floor, one for the girls and one for our parents, and above, a long attic room where the boys slept. The boys' room always had an extra bed made up for my brother Stan who was away at sea for months at a time. When I was small and he did appear, I had to be reminded he was my brother.

I loved our bedroom. We had two big double beds with feather mattresses and bolsters and exquisitely embroidered pillow cases and sheets. The wash-stand was of pink and blue marble and the jug and basin were decorated with pink swans swimming on a blue lake. The dressing table which stood at the foot of the beds had a large mirror flanked by two smaller ones; sometimes we would sit up in bed and pull dreadful faces at each other.

Early this Sunday morning, Charlotte woke me up. It was still dark.

'Millie, Millie, wake up,' she hissed in my ear. I opened my eyes, startled but not frightened. We were together in one bed, lying on our sides facing the window. Charlotte had an arm round my waist.

'What's the matter,' I whispered, 'are you ill?'

'Shush! Listen,' she muttered in my ear. I turned slowly on my back, the bed creaked slightly. For a moment I heard nothing.

'What is there to ....'

'Shush!'

And then I heard it. Two thumps as though something had fallen down in the next room followed by little evil slithering noises and a click. Then there was silence.

My sister and I clutched each other and buried our heads in our pillows. I was absolutely petrified. Our sisters Daisy and Ada slept on unheeding in the next bed. How thankful I was to have Charlotte. I heard her say softly, 'There's one more.'

One more what? I lifted my head off the pillow only to cower down as I heard a shuffling sound and a dull knocking. Then silence.

Lottie sighed and rolled over. 'That's all I heard,' she whispered. 'It's getting lighter now, shall we wake up Pa?'

I was thoroughly frightened and bathed in the sweat of fear but the idea of going into my parents' room uninvited and then to wake them up!!! All of a sudden my heart stopped thudding. I was quite safe where I was. How could noises hurt me?

'What would Pa say? "Who's making that noise? Be quiet!" We could shout that out ourselves,' and we started to giggle. We decided to tell the others in the morning.

'Pooh, those noises in the passage?' said Ada scornfully. 'Been going on for ages. Absolutely nothing. Trick of the wind, Pa says.'

'Pa says?' I echoed. So they all knew. Ada smiled her superior smile.

'Now, Ada', chided Daisy. 'You know you were frightened when you heard them first. You see,' she told Lottie and me, 'When the noises woke us up, oh, ages ago, we also heard Ma and Pa get up to find out where the noises were coming from.'

'The cupboard by the door in our room,' said I.

'The passage outside,' said Lottie.

'Well, we saw their candle flickering up and down outside in the passage. They never came in. Ma kept saying, "It will wake the children," and Pa said, "What will wake the children? There's nothing here."He sounded quite cross.'

Ada yawned. 'It doesn't bother us now. The boys say it's a ghost.'

I shuddered. 'Ghost? I'll tell Ma you're scaring me.'

'No, I'm not,' said Ada, 'You heard it yourself. Why be scared of a few old noises?'

'The boys know then, too,' said Lottie sadly. 'Seems we were the only ones who didn't know, Millie.'

After that, whenever I woke up and heard the eerie noises, I would tell myself firmly it was a trick of the wind.

Then one day my brother Stan came home. He had a friend with him who was to stay, another young seaman. I was not quite so shy of Stan as I used to be, and I liked his friend's lovely curly brown hair. My brother had a large navy sack like a bolster. When he arrived he would leave it in the middle of the room and say nothing about it till Father would remark, 'I expect you've brought home a present for your mother.' That was the signal for Stan to untie the rope fastening and bring out not only Mother's present but gifts for all of us.

In all my long life I have never forgotten the look of pleasure on his face as he gave us our gifts; he must have spent all his money on them, he never seemed to have any spare cash.

He knew about the ghostly noises; someone had certainly told him in a letter. It was a pity he had not mentioned them to his friend Owen, who heard them one night when they were particularly loud, and became extremely alarmed.

'Aren't you going to do anything about them?' he asked nervously at breakfast next morning.

'Whatever for?' answered Father. 'A mere sound shouldn't worry us, we have more character than that.'

'But the house might be falling down, er, beetles in the woodwork,' said the sailor. 'Oh, I beg your pardon, sir, I had no wish to criticise,' he added hastily. Father was staring at him.

Father, however was not staring at him in disapproval but because this solution was an idea that had not occurred to him. The thought that the fabric of the house might be in danger was disturbing.

'This must be looked into,' he announced, and being Father he wasted no time and started straight away. He called his sons to his side and accompanied by Owen they all went upstairs to examine the passage thoroughly. They lifted a few floorboards which proved to be in good condition, so they replaced them and then tackled the walls, sounding every inch. The walls were wooden planks from the floor to half their height, not elegant wainscot but plain painted boards, and above them plasterwork covered with leatherette wallpaper. They searched diligently. Stan took out his penknife when he felt an irregularity under the paper

'Do you think I might see what the ridge is? I'll have to look underneath, it will mean tearing the paper.' Father told him to go ahead.

'Our cupboard's behind that wall,' said Daisy helpfully. We four girls and Mother were hovering in the background. I fleetingly thought 'What about the shop?' but as the youngest I could justly feel it was not my place to point out that our customers might be kept waiting.

Father, who had been watching Stan slitting the wallpaper with his knife, decided he would like to do that and sent Stan and Owen to look at the cupboard behind the walls.

Suddenly I thought of something and began to jump up and down. 'Mother, the shelves! they aren't so deep at the top!'

Mother gasped. 'You're quite right, Millie. That extra space must be somewhere.' Stan and Owen, who had discovered that the top half of the cupboard was shallower than the rest at the same time that I thought about it, came out to report their find.

Father had uncovered some of the wall, tearing back the wallpaper. This revealed an oblong piece of wood set in the plaster. He started to lever it away.

'Oooh, whatever will we find?' shuddered Lottie. She was standing by me hugging Mother, we all seemed to be clinging to each other and to Mother.

Father glanced at us. He looked grim. 'Well, we can't stop now.' Gradually he worked at the panel. It gave way and fell with a clatter to the floor. A horrible musty smell floated on to the air from the hole in the wall. I felt terribly cold and began to tremble. The other girls looked sick with fear.

Mother made a quick decision. 'I don't want the girls to see. Cover your eyes, you must not look. Come, downstairs all of you.' She shepherded us away, including my youngest brother Frank who was very annoyed. We girls ran headlong down the stairs and waited in silence till Father and the boys came down. Stan was carrying a bundle; Mother wouldn't let him put it on the table till she had covered it thickly with newspaper. We eyed it solemnly, we knew instinctively that this was the cause of those ghostly slitherings, the dull thuds and the slow knocking. Owen had carried the panel down, it had a catch on it, I heard again in my mind the sinister click in the night.

We were not allowed to examine the bundle, a dirty grey linen bag tied with a tarred rope. I could not have brought myself to touch it, though I stared at the grotesque bulges with fascination.

Father and Mother were for once at a loss. We were sent out of the room while they examined what was in the bag, and then they decided to send for the police and the minister. We learned later that the bag had contained bones, human remains, the skull with teeth still attached. The police were not interested, not in a professional way that is, after the bones had been seen by a forensic scientist and pronounced to be centuries old. Our minister buried the bones and blessed the house and the ghostly sounds were hushed forever.

Although nobody could identify the bones Stan and Owen hazarded a guess that they belonged to a seaman, or that a seaman had put them there. They had noticed that the coarse linen canvas was most likely sailcloth, and there were some eyelet holes in it, so they thought the rough bag was fashioned from a sail. We agreed with him. Certainly the night before we found the bones the knocking had been particularly loud. Perhaps the ghost sailor had wanted desperately the living sailors to hear his soul's distress, that he knew they would take pity on him who had shared the dangers of the sea, find his remains and give him peace.

We never put anything else in the cupboard. It was sealed up again and disappeared behind new wallpaper.

This is the story told to me by an old friend from the Blue House in Frome. The bones were discovered in the house where she lived as a child.

MISPLACED MONEY MATTERS

When our childhood spent in family strife was over, my sister Sophie and I parted to go our separate ways. and found to our surprise that we enjoyed exchanging the occasional visit now that we could, as soon as the atmosphere between us became negatively charged, step back into our different lives and forget all about each other.

I had avoided marriage. I want a great deal of my own way, and it is easier to please yourself when there is no one else to consider. Sophie did marry; her husband is a seaman, and goes away for months at a time. Now that their two children are at boarding school, she gets restless; this might be the reason they are forever moving house, which provides a diversion for me as I am always invited down to inspect the new home.

'It's time we met again,' Sophie will write in a letter. Automatically I expect the next phrase: 'Do come and see our new house.' Though I may sigh, I make the necessary arrangements to go. It does save me the trouble of issuing an invitation.

Over the years they have moved up and down the country. I have had very little trouble in finding Sophie's new address, as she is adept at giving precise instructions. This last time I did overshoot slightly. The present upheaval had taken them into the wilds of Wiltshire, not that the countryside is wild but as I have never been farther west than Winchester, it did present me with an unconquered feeling.

I motored deeper and deeper into unfamiliar territory, the AA map and Sophie's neatly drawn diagram spread out on the seat beside me. Though it was still cold, the sunshine infected me with cheerfulness, I loved the colourful spring blossom and the unbelievable green of the fields and hills. Reaching the crossroads marked on the map I turned left and looked for the first house along

13

the lane. I found a modern, squarely-built house flanked by two garages standing in a wonderfully well-kept garden. I decided, as I got out of the car, that Sophie's husband must be earning more than I calculated. I rang the bell.

The door beyond the porch was opened by a perfect stranger. 'Can I help you?' she said. The accent in her voice I could not place. My first thought, in spite of the fact that this lady was wearing a well-cut original trouser suit which would not have looked out of place in Oxford Street, was that Sophie must be employing another au pair girl; she did not like doing her own housework. I hoped she might prove more reliable than the last one, who was asked to leave after a month when Sophie tired of getting up early in order to make the tea to wake up the girl, a very heavy sleeper.

After a few words my mistake was made plain - I had already passed my sister's house. I apologised for disturbing the peace, got back in my car and reversed up the lane. A certain peevishness settled over me when I viewed Sophie's choice. It was a thatched cottage - no wonder I had missed it, the roof was so low it was inseparable from the surrounding trees and bushes. Foreboding swept over me as I went up the path. My sister was waiting at the door, she had been watching from the window and had seen me go by.

'Well, what do you think of the house?' she asked. 'The children are going to love it, it's centuries old.'

'Certainly different,' I remarked cautiously. When I got inside I saw a long, low room with beams in the ceiling, an unnaturally large stone mantelpiece and windows with tiny panes. I admitted, as Sophie proudly showed me round, that there was a snug feeling of security about the place. My sister had lit a fire of logs in the hearth, a wonderfully welcoming sight.

'Are you insured against fire?' I asked.

Sophie giggled delightedly. 'Still the same old gloomy guts, I see. Now, while you're here, I want you to help me, there is heaps to do. We have got to go and buy material for window seats, they're so worn and shabby.'

She made me some tea and we sat and talked, filling in the mosaics missing from our lives since we last met. We walked into the village but could not buy any material: my sister was rather optimistic to expect to find a well-stocked draper's shop in the middle of nowhere. We decided to drive into Salisbury the following day - we had left it too late to fit in the expedition today, the journey was about an hour.

Back in the cottage Sophie asked me if I would mind sleeping on the sofa. 'The ceilings in the bedroom have just been replastered' she explained. 'My room is all right but the others havn't dried out properly, they're still damp and I know you are ....'

'A fussy old fool,' I finished. 'You're quite right, I don't mind about the sofa, you should know that.' It would not be the first time I had a makeshift bed under Sophie's roof, I had once been invited when the builders were still at work.

The sofa was an old-fashioned chesterfield, comfortably upholstered. I had a good night's sleep on it, waking up only once. I dimly saw Sophie in the room with a lighted candle and heard the chink of coins. I thought she must be putting some money in the electricity meter, perhaps the electricity had run out and that was why she was using a candle. She could have waited till morning. I did not rouse up sufficiently to speak.

Before we went to Salisbury to buy the material we cleared out the window seats. There were three of them, padded cushions with valances set on little lidded cupboards. Sophie had never bothered to inspect them thoroughly but I peered inside while we were measuring up. I held my tongue about their neglected state. My sister saw by my face that I was not impressed, had a look herself and promptly took action. I would have shoved all the bits of rubbish into a plastic bag straight away, but Sophie was the kind who sorted. She found a quill pen, well, it was certainly the end of a feather stuck in a plait, a couple of belts and a squashed felt hat, mouldy pieces of paper in a tatty cardboard box, a broken doll, an old purse and some things that defied identity.

'These might be valuable,' she said hopefully.

'They are rubbish,' I told her firmly. 'Just because a thing is old it need not have value. It has to be perfect to be considered antique, not worn out and rotten.'

'That's been a nice purse in its day,' she insisted. 'Look, it has been crocheted, and it must have had a pretty clasp.'

I inspected it more closely. 'Not much of the clasp left to judge.' The purse was green, worn with time and use, and showed the outlines of long gone coins in dirty relief.

'It has been shaped with different sized hooks, I think,' said Sophie. 'It has been left around a long time with the same money in it, look, the bulge is still there.'

'Throw it away,' I urged.

She sorted through the rest of the junk. We decided the stamps on the letters in the cardboard box might just be valuable; the ink on the paper had run so we could not decipher them, but the postmark on one was plain and dated from the First World War, and the stamps were obviously French. I know nothing about stamps but my sister said her children did. The rubbish disappeared into a plastic bag, the purse was left on the mantelpiece and the place smelt of Dettol when we had scrubbed out the inside of the cupboards.

We went to Salisbury and made a satisfying tour of the market and shops. There was plenty to choose from; Sophie was torn between an excellent fabric on a stall and a very good but expensive tapestry in Debenhams. The tapestry won, I knew it would, though to be fair the colours did match the rest of her furnishings better than the cheaper cloth. I was non-committal when she asked my opinion, the large flowers were too blowzy for me, but she, not I, was going to live with them.

That night before I settled down I asked Sophie if there was enough money in the electricity meter - 'You don't want to come down again in the middle of the night, candles can be dangerous.'

My sister stared at me. 'What are you talking about? It's a quarterly meter. I have not got a single candle in the house.'

I told her what I had seen and we decided I must have been dreaming. I was very tired, all this country air no doubt. I went to sleep almost immediately. I must have slept a few hours when I was suddenly awake. The fire was out but there was a bright light in the room. It came from a lighted candle in the doorway, supported in an old-fashioned candle holder. I goggled at it, fascinated, remembering Sophie's denial. Slowly the candle advanced, the light falling and moving. It was held aloft by a bony hand; my eyes focused and I became aware of a shape. Then, by the light of the candle I saw a woman in a white gown coming relentlessly towards me. I was petrified, staring in horror at the lifeless eyes and expression of malevolence on the gaunt features. She turned aside, seeming to be searching for something. I lay motionless in an icy sweat. She turned back towards me coming nearer and nearer, the candle flickering. I crossed my arms over my face to keep away the evil and then I must have fainted, for the next thing I remembered was the sun streaming through the windows. I was wet with perspiration, every bone in my body ached as though I had lain tense all night.

Gingerly I got up from the sofa and tottered to the kitchen. Sophie was already there, making the breakfast. I could not bring myself to talk about my experience. Why make her afraid - she was going to have to live with a ghost as well as the blowzy flowers. She could see I felt dreadful and was most concerned.

'It was a dream, just a bad dream,' I assured her, without going into details. I had a job to stop my teeth chattering when I thought about the apparition.

'You've been working too hard,' said Sophie briskly. 'That's what it is. You probably came away for a few days just in time, why, you might have landed up with a nervous breakdown.' I was on the point of asking if I could share the big double bed that night - we used to sleep together when we were children - but a foolish fear of being thought ridiculous restrained me.

Slowly I pulled myself together. Sophie lit the fire and tidied the room. She came across the green purse and I thought she was going to throw it into the fire after all. She could not; she quickly slipped it back into the window seat while I pretended not to notice. Gradually my fear faded.

That day we went to tea with her neighbours up the lane. The lady I had met was the daughter of the house. They were two Americans. The mother had lived in this part of the world for many years, but the daughter spent most of her time in America with relatives. They both liked Sophie and hoped she would stay, asking how she enjoyed living in her quaint little haunted house.'

My face froze, but my sister laughed and told our hostess she must not take any notice of village gossip. The cottage was a delightful place, no spooks at all. The American lady was going to argue; after all, if she had lived here for a long time she must have heard more than one tale; but she thought better of it and changed the subject.

Philosophically I faced the prospect of another night with the ghost, heroically determined not to upset my sister's tranquillity. I could do this because I swallowed a Mogadon, there is nothing like a twentieth century pill for blotting out ghostly intruders from the past.

It worked, almost. I slept mostly the sleep of the unconcious, but at one point my drugged eyes opened. I was incapable of any other movement. I saw the candle first, then the ghost. They passed me by. With a great effort, like filming in slow motion, I moved my eyes to follow them. The ghost put down the candle and bent over the window seat. The effort was too much of a struggle, my weighted eyelids closed. Centuries seemed to pass, I floated in a limbo, but through the mists I heard the chink of coins. I turned, safely cocooned by the Mogadon from any feeling of terror. I finally fell into a proper sleep.

'No dreams last night then?,' asked Sophie when she brought me a cup of tea in the morning. I sat up and thanked her, then settled back against my pillows. I was in two minds whether to tell her about the ghostly miser; she seemed totally unaware of any strange manifestations. I had to give her a warning though, somehow put her on her guard without frightening her. It was an awkward problem. Before I left I thought I solved it by asking her to promise me to leave the old green purse where it was. She looked at me reproachfully, she supposed I was being sarcastic.

A neighbour's niece actually owned the house haunted by the candle ghost and her brother-in-law saw the apparition.

ONG-B

LODGED IN THE WOOD

As I walked away from the library I was diverted to see a group of gaily dressed Cavaliers and their ladies on the bridge by the river. We do see some rare sights in our little town; I remember witnessing one Monday morning the progress of enormous green and white chess men on tow along Bath Street. These had been intended for a carnival float; I supposed the Cavaliers were rehearsing for something like that. One of them was beating on a drum, so I was encouraged to inspect the placard his fellow was carrying, which invited me to attend a Civil War battle to be enacted that afternoon on the Cheese Show field.

I did not feel equal to going alone; my husband might be interested enough to come, but if not, I would go with my neighbour Clare; she never missed anything like that. A practical thought crossed my mind: I would have been a Roundhead, wherever would I have got the money to spend on the lavish finery which identified the Cavaliers?

My husband did not want to go, so I went next door to see Clare. We live in a row of newly built council houses; they are very well designed but the gardens will take a while to settle down. I believe there was a terrible fuss when they were built, as a small copse of beech trees had to be felled - the selling price had included the value of the timber. There were a great many people who loved the trees and did not want them to be felled and the roots hauled up. All this happened before we settled here; my husband could remember the trees, as he had spent his childhood in the town.

I asked Clare if she wanted to see the battle.

'Indeed I do,' she said, 'and after last night I'm glad to be able to take the children out somewhere so they can forget.'

'Forget what?'

'I'll tell you on the way, it's a long story.' Clare knows she has a knack of

19

making a long story longer.

When she told me the tale as we walked along I did not believe her. She said that last night her two boys had been frightened by a man in their bedroom, they described him as a little thin man with terrible bags under his eyes, he was wearing a brown suit which did not fit and he had no collar or tie.

'This isn't the first time either.' It surprised me to learn that Clare put up with the situation, though I could tell from her voice she was worried.

'How does he get up to the bedroom without your knowing?' I asked. 'Tell him to go away. Call your husband, why not send for the police?'

'You don't understand. He is not really there, he is a ghost, I can't see him but the children can, and last night he started to throw things across the room. '

She could see the disbelief in my face. 'Just wait - you can come in and see for yourself one of these nights. I thought the boys were making it up, they told me about this little man, how he moved things about, but as their room is always in such a mess I couldn't tell one way or the other. They didn't seem frightened of him though, till last night.'

I wanted to question the boys but they had run on ahead. 'Well, why were they frightened last night?'

'This is the first time he actually threw something - we heard it downstairs, two big thumps. I ran up to tell them off, I thought they were larking about, but they were both tucked up in their beds and two drawers were on the floor, clean clothes everywhere. And they were scared stiff. I had to sit with them till they went to sleep.'

'But new houses don't get haunted,' I argued. 'I bet the boys did it all themselves.'

'Well, if he comes again to make mischief I shall call for you,' said Clare. 'Middle of the night even. My husband says we should call on the Vicar, but we don't go to church. I'm going to ask my Auntie Flo to tell her friend who is supposed to be a medium, interested in psychic research or something, maybe she'll come and look.'

'Can she get rid of ghosts?' I asked. But as we had reached the show field we both found more interest in the crowds, and dropped the subject. The Cavaliers and Roundheads surged up and down on the green grass enjoying themselves hugely, though the onlookers were a little bemused by the goings-on. We did not expect blood to actually flow, but we would not have been disappointed if it had.

'One way of spending Saturday afternoon, I suppose,' was all my husband said when I told him about the battle. Nettled by his indifference, I tried to prod him into some sort of reaction by telling him about Clare's ghost, but he was not interested in that either.

'Wait till it comes again,' I warned, 'we are going to be sent for.'

My husband raised his eyebrows, 'I can wait', he said.

I was too impatient to wait. I told Clare I wanted to be there when the medium came, Auntie Flo was the organising sort who would have her friend briefed in no time. Three days later she came, Miss Croker was her name. That evening seven people crowded into the small bedroom, interested neighbours like myself, but we were told to go back downstairs.

'I must be silent and concentrate,' Miss Croker informed us, so we backed down to the bottom of the stairs, stifling our giggles. The two boys Tommy and Brian were sent for - 'Never around when I want them', said their mother. We made way for them when they arrived and went upstairs, ordinary little lads in jeans and T-shirts. They went into the room, Clare came out, she shut the door and we waited. We urged her to come to us but the medium called out, 'Be quiet', so we all fell silent. Clare stayed where she was. My back began to ache after a, while, so I sat down on the stairs.

We were all still waiting when Big Brian came in, understandably startled to find his home invaded by so many neighbours.

'What's all this?' he asked. Clare hurried down.

'Ssh, I'll get you your supper,' she hissed. 'You would come back early just when I didn't want you to!'

Big Brian looked hurt. 'What's going on?'

'It's the spirit lady, she's here.'

Her husband stiffened. 'I told you I didn't want her in my house.' He started to walk towards the stairs but Clare hustled him into the kitchen and closed the door. We could hear them arguing and the muffled sounds of a meal being got ready; it made a change from listening to nothing going on upstairs.

Then - a cry from the bedroom, a horrified scream. We quivered with shock, the quarrel went on in the kitchen. Two distinct thuds from upstairs. I grew frightened, we ought to do something. I saw sweat break out on Mrs Symon's face - she was the lady who lived the other side of Clare. She mouthed, 'I don't want Miss Croker to move the spirit away, it might go next door.' I never thought of that. Suddenly I was convinced the whole thing was true, the boys were not making it up.

Big Brian burst from the kitchen, a wailing Clare in his wake. He strode upstairs and pushed open the bedroom door.

'I'm not having this, I must ask you to go,' he said firmly, taking his sons in his arms. The medium came out, still almost in a trance, her eyes shining.

'Oh, Mr Foster, now you have disturbed us, but it was a most rewarding experience.'

A babble of voices broke out - 'Well, tell us!' 'We've been waiting'. 'Whatever happened?' but Big Brian quelled the sound.

'You can all go home,' he said in the loudest voice of all, grimly determined to be master in his own house.

'Don't be so awful, Brian, I asked them to come,' protested Clare, but in no time at all we found ourselves halfway down the garden path. Auntie Flo held her ground and stayed with Clare. I took the bewildered Miss Croker by the arm.

'Do forgive us,' I said coaxingly. 'You can see Mr Foster is a little upset. Won't you come to my house for a cup of tea, you must be quite shattered.'

Miss Croker accepted my invitation, she could see Clare had other problems to cope with. A few neighbours included themselves in my offer of hospitality, so five of us settled down to tea and biscuits in my house. My husband obligingly turned the television off and we were ready to hear Miss Croker's story.

I must admit I had been disappointed in the lady's style of dress, I had thought all mediums would be flamboyantly dressed in scarves and floating draperies. Miss Croker was neatly attired in a Welsh tweed suit of maroon and light blue with navy blue court shoes. Her story was to make up for what she lacked in appearance.

'When I first went into the room I felt an overwhelming sadness,' she told us, her thin, beringed hands clasped tightly round her cup. 'It was most incredible. This feeling was particularly intense by the window. It seemed to increase when the boys came in. They did not look at me; I asked them what they could see, and they described the being they had already told their Mother about.' She broke off to drink some tea. 'Then I stepped towards this sensation of despair. I came up against an unseen barrier; I put up my hands to move it, I felt a weight yield and then swing back. I realised suddenly, I think I screamed ....' She looked at us solemnly. 'There is a body hanging in that room. I think the spirit the children can see there was once a man who hanged himself.'

None of us doubted the truth of what she said, we were all horrified. After everyone had gone, even my husband did not scoff as I was afraid he might. 'How could anyone hang themselves without the Fosters knowing? I asked. 'They are the first tenants in that house.'

'I think it happened a long time ago,' answered my husband. 'Remember what was there before, the trees?' He stayed thoughtful for a while, then said, 'Think we'll go and see my Dad tomorrow, tell him about it.'

My Father-in-law I loved dearly. He was a placid wise old countryman who, when his wife had died, calmly accepted the situation that he could not stay on his own. He refused to live with any of his children, all of whom would have been glad to have him, and settled instead in a little flat run by a warden, 'Sheltered Accommodation' was what his doctor called it. We visited him regularly, I wondered for a minute why my husband suggested it now, then I picked up his line of thought. The old man was well into his nineties and may have heard in his youth some story to account for the ghost.

We went to visit him the following evening, and he listened in silence as we told him the story.

'Have you ever heard anything about a hanging, Dad? Something that happened a long time ago in that wood?' I asked.

He hesitated, tapping out his pipe over the hearth - it was an empty hearth now in these days of central heating, but the warden had thoughfully provided a waste paper basket and I doubt if Dad noticed the difference when he was deep in thought.

Then he sighed. 'Poor old soul. Not much luck in life and not much in death, or after death I should say. I can remember when I was about 11, they cut a man down from one of those trees. Crawley, that was his name, Jonathan Crawley. His wife had left him.' He paused, began to say something and then fell into the easy sleep of extreme old age.

'Well, at least you've got a name and a date for Clare,' said my husband as we waited for him to wake up again. 'You could look it up in the newspaper files.'

I wondered whether to but I did not. My feelings of pity and sorrow were struggling with indignation. Why on earth take your own life because some woman had left you; by no stretch of the imagination could I see my husband doing it, though I could not see myself leaving him to find out.

No, it was up to Clare and Brian to do any more investigating, it was their ghost. They said they were going to leave it all to the vicar.

My eldest daughter told me about the hanging ghost as her friend's sister lived in the house he haunted. The family were greatly troubled by the unhappy spirit and asked to be rehoused.

ROOTED TO THE PAST

Radstock has always seemed to me to be a pleasant little town, not at all deserving of the title, *The Wigan of Somerset*. I had the opportunity to explore the place when I used to travel to Wells by bus once a fortnight. I changed at Radstock and there is half an hour's wait between the time the bus gets in from my village and the departure of the bus to Wells. Sometimes I would go to the Community Hall, open most mornings for coffee, provided in turn by the ladies of the various churches. The helpers in charge on my day served lovely coffee. I got to know most of them, one in particular, Dottie Hardcastle; she became a firm friend when we discovered we were both interested in bonsai trees.

'Would you like to come and see my collection?' she asked one day. I certainly wanted to but the difficulty was when. It was an effort for me to make this visit regularly to Wells; I went to see my house-bound aunt, she was not ill exactly, just very old and disinterested in the outside world. My job was in Bath and then there was the family to look after and the garden and then the house. My sense of duty struggled with the temptation to build up a new friendship.

'Love to come, Dottie, but I can't really find the time what with one thing and another. Wouldn't like my aunt to feel neglected.'

'Are you the only one who goes to see her? No other relatives?' enquired Dottie.

'There's my cousins,' I answered thoughtfully. When I came to think about the situation, why should I be the only one of the family to support my aunt? It did seem to me that lately I detected a certain irritability in the old lady's manner, she was surely becoming bored with my visits. I decided to appeal to my cousins. They both lead very varied lives, Barbara helps her husband with his market garden besides working three mornings a week in a dress shop - she must meet heaps of different people - and Muriel runs a playgroup and collects

25

coloured glass. All those auctions she attends must provide many a tale to entertain Auntie.

After several telephone calls they reluctantly agreed to share my task of calling to see the old lady.

'Once in a while,' offered Muriel.

'Once every six weeks at least,' I said firmly. 'After all, you can drive yourself there, and I have to go by bus.' The three of us worked out a rota and I could now spend some time going to see Dottie without my conscience nagging me.

Dottie's bonsai collection was outstanding. She had inherited her father-in-law's carefully tended treasures and more specimens had been bought to add to them over the years. I noticed they were all in traditional half-glazed shallow containers, not a plastic pot to be seen.

'Stan's father started collecting when he was left these three little trees,' and Dottie pointed them out. 'They had belonged to his father and they were very old then. We decided to have this terrace built specially for them.' The little trees spent most of their time on the terrace, a sort of rockery with flat stones waist high from the ground. One or two trees would be selected now and again for a short display as house plants.

Now my own collection was a far more more haphazard affair. For many years I had admired bonsai trees when I saw them, retreating hastily when I saw the price they commanded. Then one year I happened to notice some little oak trees growing in a corner of our garden, the children had once played there with some acorns they had collected on one of our walks. It was unthinkable to uproot them callously and burn them, but our garden is too overcrowded for one oak tree never mind the eleven so trustingly pushing their little trunks above the soil. I set about finding homes for them all, well, gardens really. Not many people are keen to have great big trees on their property - 'Roots spread', pointed out a dear neighbour. I managed to place seven of my little space invaders. I dug out the remaining four and set them in pots, hopeful that some day they would be wanted. Meanwhile I absently trimmed the roots that poked their way through the drain holes.

So it began. Ash trees and sycamores have joined those four little oaks, two elder trees, an orange and a grapefruit grown from pips, and a plum tree grown from a stone. There are two lilacs and two wistaria grown by air-layering our own trees. I failed using this method on the old apple tree though. They will not be true bonsai for years yet but I am willing to wait, and am concentrating on keeping them alive at the moment.

Dottie was very kind about my efforts and gave me several hints, though she cannot have been all that impressed.

'Sad to think I'll never see them at their best,' I sighed. 'Mustn't be discouraged , though.'

'After all, we can look at the results of trees planted a long time ago,' said Dottie wisely. 'The people who planted them couldn't have our pleasure in the results.'

'Miniature Capability Browns we must be,' I agreed. 'Still, they give me a great deal of satisfaction sometimes.'

'Er, I don't like the look of this one.' My friend picked up a wilting sycamore. 'Though perhaps all it needs is a little more water.' I fetched my watering-can ready filled with rain water at once. 'There now, I must have missed this one.' Carefully I gave the plant water in little sips, then as the weather was dry and hot Dottie helped me to spray the whole lot.

'How do you manage when you go away?' I asked. 'One of my children is always on hand to help with the watering. Will your children come back now they are married and living away, or do the neighbours help?'

'Yes, Celia will come over and Jason as well. I can't rely on our neighbours.'

'Not very neighbourly then? Can't imagine you having trouble with anyone ....'

'Oh, it's nothing like that, they are all very nice people,' Dottie handed me the water spray and we walked back indoors. 'It's the house you see. It has the reputation for being haunted. They won't go in if we aren't there.'

'Well!' I was intrigued by the idea of living in a haunted house. 'When did you find this out?'

'Long before I was married and went to live there. It's well known in Radstock, the house has always been pointed out as the one with the ghost. When I met Stan though, he told me it was rubbish. His family have lived there for generations so he should know, and I've not bothered about it since. I love living there, and Stan certainly wouldn't dream of leaving.'

Dottie did not say any more but when I next went to the house I stared around me on the alert for any signs of a ghost. I was disappointed. The plain Georgian house, built with solid thick stone walls, enveloped one in comfort and security, the furnishings and quiet colours echoed the same soothing atmosphere. Dottie obviously had a feeling for harmony in the things she had chosen for the house, though I expect a great deal had been already there. Stan did not have a very well-paid job but with an inherited house and all that went with it, a love of old things and no desire for new, he and Dottie had few worries.

The idea that the house was haunted began to seem as preposterous to me as it was to Dottie. That summer went warmly by. I was thankful I had got out of the rut of seeing my aunt so faithfully. She eventually died and left all her money to Barbara and her ornaments and furniture to Muriel.

It was on a lovely day, almost autumn, that I changed my mind. I was over at Radstock and Dottie asked me if I would like some spinach. I accepted her offer, we had eaten all of ours, so we went into the garden. Dottie began to gather the leaves while I stood by the terrace admiring the little bonsai trees.

We had got used to the warm sunlit days. I was wearing a sleeveless dress and then, as I bent closer to study the trees more closely I began to shiver. I hugged myself and rubbed my bare arms, the flesh was covered in goosepimples. A nasty little breeze seemed to be blowing. There was someone else standing by the terrace - now my husband says I saw what I did because of my imagination and wanting to see something - I will swear I distinctly saw a lady actually holding one of the oldest trees in its beautiful shallow pot, turning it slowly in her hands. I glanced wildly towards Dottie, bending unawares over the spinach, and then back again at my companion. She had curly hair brushed up in ringlets and held in black ribbon. Her gown was long and grey with a high waist and narrow sleeves topped with little black puffs, frilled with black lace at the wrists. Deep black ruffles fringed the skirt. I felt so sad all at once, all miserable and somehow drained.

Deep silence was all around me. The lady put the tree down and moved away. Slowly she drifted along the path and as I watched I could see the wall through her. A black flounce floated over the ground and then there was no one there.

Dottie came over with the spinach and I pulled myself together. My first thought as my misery left me was, whatever was there to be frightened of? The warmth came back, the sun was still shining and Dottie obviously had seen nothing at all. It was time for me to go so I thanked my friend for the spinach, now safely stowed in a plastic bag, and set off to catch my bus.

It was very hard to stop thinking about what I had seen - 'what you thought you saw,' insisted my husband. Then he relented and suggested that I should read something about the history of Radstock and see if I could find any local character who would fit my description of the lady.

'Go to the library,' he urged. 'Or maybe ask someone who has lived in Radstock for a long time - those helpers at the place you used to go to for coffee might know all about it.'

It was a good idea, but now that I visited Dottie I rarely went to the Community Hall. There must be some history of the house in archives somewhere, but I just could not bring myself to ferret around: it seemed to me to be very rude to be curious about my friend's house behind her back. She had said categorically there was no ghost according to her husband who, as the heir to the family which had lived there for donkeys' years, was in the best position to know.

Not long afterwards my husband and I were invited to celebrate Stan and Dottie's twenty-fifth wedding anniversary - they were going to hold an evening party at home for their family and friends.

'If we don't do something ourselves I know Celia and Jason will put their heads together and arrange a gathering of the clans. They really are very sweet and it would all be far too expensive for them. I would rather invite people we want and not relations the children think we want,' explained Dottie when I accepted the invitation. Indeed I knew my friend was firm about spending her time the way she wanted to, all of it; now and then I wondered why she bothered with me, but we did have the same sense of humour.

The matter of what to give as a suitable present now occupied my mind. At first I thought of another bonsai tree in a silver container but I suspected that would be the idea of quite a few of those going to the party. Usually for the silver weddings that have come our way I do some embroidery with silver thread or crochet a set of mats with a silver line running through them. I had almost decided to make cushions with raised silver roses but it was debatable whether they could be finished in time. The easiest solution was to buy something silver, so I went round the shops in Bath to see what they had to offer, taking a few hours off work.

Luckily enough, I met Celia, Dottie's daughter; mind you, I knew she did her shopping in Bath on a Tuesday afternoon so I had chosen that day especially. She was carrying her first child, still only a few months old, in one of those sling things around her neck. All young mothers seem to do it, though I wondered how on earth the children managed to be comfortable. Still, it was none of my business and my ideas about babies are very old-fashioned.

I asked Celia if she had time to talk about my problem of what to give her parents. She said, yes, she would be willing to listen. The baby was sleeping, no trouble at all, so we went to have some coffee in Owen Owen's ground floor coffee shop. I fetched the coffee while Celia sat down and carefully disposed the baby on her lap. I watched the young man behind the counter as he gently spooned chocolate over the frothy coffee, thinking how odd it was I always drank coffee away from home but was a dedicated tea drinker once I got back.

Celia was no help at all. I outlined my choices, delicately hinting that I could afford as much as was needed, which was true.

'Why, Mrs Rainbow, they all seem perfectly appropriate, I am sure Mummy and Daddy will be pleased with any of them,' Celia smiled at me indulgently. She must have thought of me as an old fuss-pot.

'Well, it was kind of you to come and listen to me,' said I. 'By the way,' - I suddenly realised I could ask Celia about the apparition, she would know the family history- 'Is your parents' house really haunted?'

Celia seemed amused. 'Now, why do you ask? Been listening to local folk tales?' Her face changed when I told her, in detail, what I had seen.

'How very odd! Well, if you promise not to tell my mother' - and I did, solemnly - 'now you've seen her, I might as well tell you.'

It was a very sad tale. Long ago, about the time we were fighting the Napoleonic Wars, the sister of Stan's great-great-grandfather had wanted to marry a soldier, a young officer. Her family had not considered him good enough for her (shades of the family who had rejected the future Iron Duke of Wellington for their daughter). She was ordered not to see him any more. Such was the passion between them they could not face life without each other, and chose death. He had shot her, then turned the gun on himself. He died but she did not and had to struggle on living.

'How terrible!' I was horrified. 'They must have been very young.'

'She must have been an absolute wet,' said the modern young woman opposite me. 'She could have used her own two feet and just walked out with him, I would have done. 'The baby in her lap showed signs of waking up, he began to stretch and wriggle. We both gazed at him fondly. 'I must be going, now remember you must not tell mother. Daddy was afraid she wouldn't marry him if he expected her to live in a haunted house. We see her, but not mummy. She is not born family.'

'Neither am I, yet I saw the unhappy young woman.'

'Can't think why that was, but please, not a word.'

'I've already promised,' I reminded Celia. 'Do you think it was because I like growing little trees?'

Celia smiled. 'Could well be,' she said. 'The last gift the officer was allowed to present to the lady in grey was the little tree he had brought all the way from India.'

The Radstock ghost is well known, and I heard about it from a historian during a conducted tour of the town.

SPIRIT TAKEOVER BID

Athene said she was going to the spiritualist for help and guidance. I said cynically, was she getting it?

'You don't understand, Nancy. My life lacks meaning somehow. I feel the need to reach out, make new contacts.'

She was right, I did not understand. It was hard to see where Athene wanted to reach to - I thought she had all she needed. She lived with her husband Peter and her two little girls very comfortably indeed. Peter had never met with redundancy in his career and now, with IBM, he was earning about four times as much as my late husband ever did. A large house luxuriously furnished, double garage and two cars bought new every two years, beautiful gardens and a gardener, what more could Athene want? Athene has one good point though, she never rubs her wealth in.

Mind you, I never boast either. I have far more friends than Athene and more people come to see me in a week than Athene has visitors in a month. I admit I did envy the ease with which she could settle her bills. I did countless little sums on odd bits of paper, would pay one thing this week with money borrowed from next week's income, and sometimes I would root through pockets and purses hoping to find the odd bank note I might have overlooked. All Athene had to do was to write a cheque, secure in the knowledge that it would be met.

Just now Athene was looking out of the window at my garden. We were sitting in my front room and I hoped she would not admire my Blue Moon roses as I would feel obliged to offer her some and I did not want to part with a single one. She was silent for some time. We had known each other since childhood, and it was a comfortable silence. I tried to think of some new contact for Athene; no use suggesting pottery classes, she doesn't like getting her hands messy.

ONG-C

'Would you like to come?'

'What, to see the spiritualist? Good Lord, no. Besides, it is forbidden by the church.' I tend to invoke religion when it suits my argument. I do practise my faith; Athene no longer does.

'No natural curiosity then?' Athene smiled at me tolerantly. 'Anyway, I feel it helps me.'

'Does Peter mind?'

'Peter? Well, I've told him, he doesn't seem to care. I don't think he ever listens to what I say.

'Now, Athene, that's not true. I'm sure he still dotes on you, same as he has always done.'

'As much as the company will let him, you mean.' She sighed, her fingers twisting the lovely gold necklace she wore. I knew Peter had given it to her for her last birthday. Then she got up, picked up her handbag and said goodbye.

'If you change your mind and want to come, I go every Wednesday.'

The weeks went by. These days, now I am a widow, I seem to be marking time. I noticed a change in Athene. She did not come to see me so often and when she did she was polite but withdrawn, there was no frankness, no real conversation at all. Another thing which distressed me, her appearance became slovenly. Her lovely hair, which had been kept glossy and curly and in tip-top condition, slowly grew past her shoulders, lank and greasy. She did not put polish on her fingernails any more, the lacquer already applied split and peeled off. Sometimes her jacket had a button missing, she wore laddered tights.

All her friends tried talking to her, but she did not take any notice of us. Then we discussed her between ourselves; it was not strictly speaking gossiping, we all genuinely wanted to help. Then she was not seen about anymore.

I could have kicked myself the day I saw her children out taking their dog for a walk. Why, they looked positively neglected! Well, I might be thought a busybody, but this could not go on. Athene must be sick. I thought of her parents, they lived the other side of Bristol and her mother had a hard life looking after her invalid father. It did not seem fair to involve them just yet. Anyway I must speak to Peter first, and I phoned him. I had seen his car in the drive so I knew he must be there.

'Aren't you worried about Athene?' I asked him bluntly. 'None of my business really, Peter, but ....'

'Nancy, I'm out of my mind, you have no idea what it's like - she won't go to see a doctor and cannot see that there's anything wrong. Come up, will you, I know it's difficult, but see if you can talk to her.'

I am handicapped, I do not walk very well, so I either drive an ordinary car specially adapted or an electric wheelchair. I can manage on crutches but not for long so I never go anywhere unless invited, as I have to be helped up steps and that kind of thing. When I knew Peter would be there to welcome me I went to see Athene.

Her appearance shocked me. She was wearing very expensive clothes, a skirt, blouse and a cardigan, but the colours were all wrong together, her zip was unfastened, her collar tucked in and she had spilt food down her front. She had lost weight and did not look clean.

'My dear, are you ill?' I said gently, tidying her up as best I could. She looked at me and mumbled something. I tried to straighten her collar but she pushed me away sharply. I looked at her and a cold chill spread over me, I did not seem to be looking at Athene at all.

'Get the doctor,' I said to Peter as I turned away. 'It is obvious we can do nothing.'

'She won't see him. He has come, mind you, but she turns sullen and locks herself in her room. He spoke of a personality disorder, I could see he thought I was wasting his time. Suggested I take her to see a psychiatrist. I'll have to take her by force, she can be violent, you can see she is not the same person .. ..' We were speaking together in whispers, the figure in the chair sat motionless and silent. Practical matters had to be settled first.

'Shall I take the children?'

'I am taking them back to school tomorrow. I'll worry about half-term when it comes.'

'Food? Housework? The dog?'

'Enough food in the house to feed an army, and I usually eat out anyway. The girls do the housework when they are here, I can take over. It's easy enough to work the Hoover and the washing machine. Dick looks after the dog.' Dick was the gardener.

'Ah well, if I can't help, at least I can pray for her.' I felt so sorry for the little family; what must those two little girls have suffered at home on holiday from their boarding school? I had seen only the fringe of all the troubles and horridness that must have arisen from trying to cope with the dirty, unwilling, lack-lustre creature at the centre of the household. Oh, Athene, what had happened? And then I remembered the spiritualist sessions. 'Peter, does Athene still go to see the spiritualist?'

'No, she stopped going some months ago.'

A little niggle started in my mind. Long ago, when Athene and I were at school together another child had once told us about a séance; one of the nuns who taught us overheard the conversation and started to question her. I remembered the concern and shock in the nun's expression. The nun was not being bossy - 'You must not do this,' and so on, laying down the law. She tried to explain as clearly as she could that we should always keep control of our minds and our will, we must never let anyone else or anything else use them. I began to wonder whether Athene was physically ill or was her mind sick? She might have stopped going to the spiritualist for help and guidance but what had happened while she was there?

Peter was clearly at his wits' end. 'I can't be here all the time - I've got my job to think of and God knows I find enough stress there as it is. I live in a nightmare.'

Over the next few days I contacted various organisations I thought might help. We set about finding a specialist who made house calls. Peter began to think of sending Athene to a private nursing home if a suitable one could be found. Then I thought of the priest, who visited me occasionally.

'Do you mind if I ask Father Maddox to call?' I asked Peter. He was surprised, though he knew Athene had once gone to church. 'Well, I can't see that it'll do any harm,' he agreed reluctantly. 'If she will see him.'

I went immediately to Father and explained the situation, trying to make him understand that I thought Athene was possessed. He was not at all sceptical and went to see her. He became convinced that here was a case for exorcism so we thought we would try that first before involving the medical profession. Generally it is the other way round.

Father Maddox made all the necessary arrangements. I believe the Bishop has to be consulted and a special priest is sent, trained to conduct the exorcism. I did not want to be present. I said I would wait in the next room to help Athene if need be.

They do work, exorcisms, properly conducted and properly blessed. Here was proof in Athene, freed from whatever it was that had possessed her mind. I saw reason plain in her face as soon as I went in to see her when the ceremony was over. She said she had been feeling very tired, she had not realised how ill she had been.

Oh, it was lovely to see my friend alert and thinking again! The relief on Peter's face, the deep love between them still there!

'I don't understand how I got so low,' said Athene, bewildered to see the priest and the candles and the incense. 'Thank you so much for calling, Father.' She told me later that she thought she had been given the Blessing of the Sick while she was unconscious.

The priest looked exhausted. He collected his things ans said quietly to Peter and me 'Athene does not realise what has been happening.' As he left the house, he added, 'You had better keep an eye on the dog for a few days.'

We had forgotten all about the dog, he had been in the room lying at Peter's feet during the exorcism. He seemed to be asleep. How strange the priest should be concerned about him.

I was concerned about him myself when I called the following day to see my friend. There was the dog, a big golden retriever, sitting outside in the middle of the road. 'Come on, Sandboy, good dog. Heel now, heel!' Instead of getting up and coming to me the dog ignored my command. I went on up the path in my car and told Athene about him when she came out to help me.

'You had better get him to move,' I warned her. 'He will be killed if a car comes down here at any speed.' Athene called to the dog but he took no notice so she went and took hold of his collar and hauled him to his feet. He snarled at her, then trotted jerkily into the garden. My friend shut the gates.

'Whatever is the matter with Sandboy? Not like him to snarl.' I struggled to my feet and managed to stand by the side of my little car. 'I'm so glad to see you better, Athene. I've brought you some roses, will you bring them in?' My friend obligingly gathered up the bunch from the basket in the car and then offered me her arm. 'They are heavenly,' she said, breathing in their perfume, 'Thank you so much Nancy.' They were not from the Blue Moon rose bush which had gone over - this variety was Peace.

We forgot about the dog. Athene declared she was fit as a fiddle and could not understand how she had allowed herself to become so neglectful. I hoped her life would resume its course and she would be thankful for what she had got and not go looking for experiences beyond.

Then the dog disappeared for a week. He came back starving, wolfed down some food and was off again. 'He must go to the vet before he goes completely wild,' a worried Athene told me.

After a few days, Sandboy was spotted near the railway station, the guard on duty knew him. It was lucky he was there as the station at Bradford on Avon is not always manned. When he had shut the dog up in the empty waiting room the guard telephoned Athene and asked her to come and fetch him. I was at Athene's when she got the message and immediately got up to go. 'Unless you would like me to come with you,' I offered. Not that I would be much use to help control the dog.

'Of course you can,' said Athene, paying me the greatest compliment she could by seeming to forget my handicap. She drove straight to the station.

The guard came over to us. 'Sandboy's not a bit like himself,' he warned Athene. 'But maybe he will calm down when he sees you.' I stayed in the car and watched while the guard and Athene went up to the building where the dog was confined. The man unlocked the door and the dog came out. Athene bent over to pat him and reach for his collar, she had his leash with her. He did not wag his tail or frisk about in welcome as he used to do. He was still for a moment then suddenly moved. He leapt past the two people trying to soothe him, streaked down the length of the platform, jumped down on the rails and made straight for the tunnel. I saw a look of horror dawn on the railwayman's face and realised what he might be saying to Athene. I looked and saw the signal lights on green. We could do nothing, the dog was in the tunnel and the oncoming train could not be stopped. The driver said later he could not truthfully say whether he felt a bump or not, he certainly did not see the dog.

I tried to comfort Athene when she came back to the car, and the guard said he would attend to everything. As we drove from the station I saw two men walking into the tunnel, they had a spade, a powerful torch and a large plastic sack. I did not envy them their task, they would see a horrible Though Athene was shocked, she was more anxious about Peter's grief; Sandboy was his dog. sack. I did not envy them their task, they would see a horrible sight. Though Athene was shocked, she was more anxious about Peter's grief; Sandboy was his dog.

'Peter will understand,' I said. I knew in my heart that whatever power had taken over my friend's mind had been driven into the dog by the force of the exorcism. It had to go somewhere.

I was even more sure when I talked to the guard later. He told me that when they had found the dog he was lying across the rails, and the wheels of the train must have gone over him. But from nose-tip to tail he was perfect, not crushed at all.

The exorcism in this tale was told by a Roman Catholic priest during the talks at a Day of Recollection at which I was present.

NOT QUITE VACANT

Flo came round the back of my house, gave a knock on the window as she passed, then came straight in the kitchen. The door is usually on the latch.

'I've come to ask you for help, Cassie,' she announced, putting two shopping bags heavily on the floor. I invited her to sit down and felt the teapot to see if it was warm enough to pour out another cup. It was not, so I got up to put the kettle on.

'Oh, what's all this then? Not like you to ask for anything,' I said. Flo was very independent. We had been friends for donkeys' years, ever since we both moved down from the north when the carpet firm we worked for decided to open a factory here. We knew each other by sight before the move; afterwards we worked side by side and found we had a lot in common. We did not lose touch when we retired, we still went on outings together. To keep ourselves occupied we found part-time jobs cleaning factories, though I soon changed mine and went to work twice a week for Mrs Maidly, a lady with a large house, a large income and five children. Flo stuck to her daily factory job, that was where she had been this morning. If she did some shopping on the way home she usually called in my place for rest after climbing the hill.

'It's a big favour, Cass,' Flo warned me as I set about making fresh tea and putting out another cup. 'But I do hope you won't say no.'

'How can I say yes or no till you've told me what you want? This will be ready in a minute, then you can come straight out with it.' I could see Flo was in a state about something. She waited till I sat down then leaned across the table to look me straight in the eye.

'Our Nora has sent me the money to go and see her in America so I want you to do my job for me while I go. There!'

I was so startled I did not know what to say. I realised the prospect of seeing her daughter must have given her great joy. It was a pity I had to be involved.

'It's like this,' my friend went on hastily before I could open my mouth, 'I need a month off to go what with all the travelling. Well, the firm closes for the usual fortnight's holiday at the end of July, that is the first two weeks for me, then I need two more extra - that's when I want you to fill in for me, then I'll be back. I'm sure my boss will agree.' She leaned back in her chair. I still did not know what to say.

'You see, I'm frightened that if the firm employs someone younger to take my place she'll get the job permanently. It would be hard for me to find a new job now,' explained Flo.

'You will have to give up one day,' I said gently.

'Ah, but not yet. Not until Don has his house paid for,' Flo sighed. Some people might think her greedy to hang on to a wage but not me. Besides her careful, saving daughter in America whom she had not seen for 15 years, Flo had a son who, with his spendthrift wife and careless children squandered every penny Flo generously gave them. They were buying a large house which they could not afford, while Flo, like myself, was content with a council house.

'Isn't it a bit cheeky to find your own replacement?' I asked, privately thinking that Flo was a bit cheeky to ask so much of me. Then I looked at her lined, shiny pink face and hopeful eyes and thought how awful it would be if my daughter lived three thousand miles away and I could not see her every week.

'Mr Lever won't mind, anyway I can but ask, same as I'm asking you.' Flo looked at me expectantly. 'I know I can rely on you, you are very thorough.'

'I can't let my own lady down,' I began and then stopped. I remembered Mrs Maidly had told me the family would be away for the whole of August and the first week in September, that meant six weeks' holiday for me but no holiday pay - indeed I had moaned about it to Flo. I could manage without the money, but extra always came in useful.

'Er, how much would I get paid?' I enquired cautiously. Flo told me, I was tempted and I made up my mind.

'All right,' I agreed. 'It's up to Mr Lever now.'

Mr Lever turned out to be the Personnel Officer and he was quite willing to go along with Flo's plan. I would take Flo's place for two weeks and her wage packets. I do not suppose Higher Management was all that concerned about the cleaning as long as the job got done. Flo was so pleased and excited now the way was clear for her prolonged holiday. 'I'll make it up to you, Cassie,' she vowed and she set about making her travelling arrangements.

In July I went along to the firm where Flo works. The building, set back from the road behind a rank of houses, was big and box-like with three long thin arched windows down the side and huge square ones at the front. There were two small extensions tacked on, one was a sloping structure at the back and the other a very small lean-to at the side, an outside toilet. Plenty of room for cars, I noticed.

Flo and I spent the morning together as she showed me how she set about her work, we both have very high standards as far as cleanliness is concerned. The firm turned out monitors of some sort and the men working in the laboratory and workshops seemed pleasant enough. We were nearly finished by the time they began to arrive, they took very little notice of us except to say 'Somebody new then?' to Flo but she did not offer any explanation. We said 'Good morning" and went on working down the corridor to the front door which was our last job. Overhearing their conversation as they passed by I was interested to learn that some engineer was expected back, 'the one who had seen the ghost.'

'What was all that about then? What ghost?' I asked Flo on our way home.

'Oh, some rubbish about a tormented old faggot who wanders round the place making weird noises. Once upon a time he could not be seen but nowadays they say you can see him vanishing through the new partition across the offices, that used to be one big room when the firm first came here. I've never seen him but there is one thing -' Flo put a hand on my arm as if to reassure herself. 'Now, you won't change your mind?'

'I promise, go on, you know I don't believe in ghosts ....'

'Well, remember the storeroom upstairs? When I've been up there all by myself I sometimes think I can hear children singing. It doesn't frighten me, it's a lovely sound. The place was built as a chapel.'

We stopped talking to cross over at the bottom of Keyford, a junction of five roads. Mercifully, as it was the time children were going to school the crossing lady was still there to help. I made a mental note of this as I hate crossing busy roads without a proper crossing, but then remembered I would be going to work in the school holidays.

Frome is a town full of old buildings with a ghost in a tidy few of them if you believed all you heard. Flo's remarks did not put me off and when the time came I quite enjoyed her cleaning job though by the end of the first week I was very tired and thankful to think I had only one more week to do.

On the Wednesday the director's secretary, Mrs Fairford, called me into her office as I was getting ready to go home.

'I hope you don't mind my asking, Mrs Wetherby,' she said, 'but can you finish early tomorrow? Some important American businessmen are coming here to look over the place, they say they should arrive at nine o'clock. Of course, we want to make a good impression ....' Quite, they did not want to see any cleaning equipment about the premises or a little old cleaner bobbing in and out.

'I shall be gone by half past eight,' I promised and turned to go but a large, fair-haired young man bounced into the room. He stood in the doorway with his hand on the knob so I could not get by.

'Have you remembered about the stores?' he asked Mrs Fairford. 'They are still in a mess. The Y.T.S. lads were trying to sort out some components and they didn't know where to look. They are off to some lecture or other today, so I can't ask them to tidy up.

Mrs Fairford smiled at me. 'You can see to that I daresay?'

'Well, not now,' I objected and then I thought if I had to finish early tomorrow I would not have time to straighten things out then. I could see the same consideration occurred to Mrs Fairford. Well, I've only one pair of hands, they should have thought of these things before. The young man offered a solution.

'Can you come back tonight?' he asked me directly. 'I'll be here till half past seven. Overtime rates of course.' So I agreed, grumpily.

I had a good rest when I went home, I did not do any of my own housework so I felt quite refreshed when I went back about six o'clock. The time of day alters the feel of a place. The building was hot and airless and the light entirely different. Mr Andrews, the fair-haired young man, had a word with me as I put my overall on. 'It's very good of you to help out like this, Mrs Wetherby. But appearances go a long way with Americans.'

Before I went upstairs to start tidying there I went through most of the rooms downstairs to neaten them up so I would have less work tomorrow. It was very hot and when I did go up to see the storerooms it was even hotter. Most of the area was tidy, all the stock in neat piles, but one corner was all higgledy-piggledy. I could see it just needed patience to straighten things out and set to work.

The upper storey of the building was divided into laboratory, toilets and the storeroom where I was working, a big spacious area lit at the side by the tall thin windows which reached right down the wall through to the floor below. The sun in the west flooded the room with brightness. It was fearfully hot, that August was to provide record temperatures. I was glad I had on my own cotton pinny instead of the nylon one provided by the firm. I worked away steadily, it was quite still but I hummed a little tune. I often do when I am on my own. I found I was singing a hymn, and quite gradually I realised I was not singing it by myself. I could hear children's voices, sweet and innocent.

'And keep us in His grace, and guide us when perplexed,
And free us from all ills, in this world and the next.'

Then I became aware of a smell, a strong burning smell. I looked around in alarm and saw smoke rising in spirals from the well stacked boxes at the other end of the room.

'Help! Fire!' I shrieked. Good Lord! was there only Mr Andrews to hear me? I remembered there was a fire extinguisher on the stairs and ran to get it. I struggled back with it still screaming. The smoke was billowing quite fiercely up the walls and little flames started to lick round the edges of the boxes. I set off the foam, and almost immediately I heard someone come up behind me - it was Mr Andrews with another extinguisher and we battled with the fire together. The smoke seemed to be subsiding slowly.

'We'd better get the Fire Brigade, go and dial 999' ordered Mr Andrews. I rushed away at once, extremely annoyed to think he had not made the call before coming to my rescue. The nearest phone was downstairs as the laboratory was kept locked so I dialled from the one in Mrs Fairford's office.

'Which service do you require?'

'Fire - we've got a fire!'

'Where are you ringing from and your number please.' I gave them the name of the firm and then the address. 'Corner of Keyford and Lock's Hill, just up the road from your station.'

'Yes, but where?'

'The old Methodist Chapel, you can't miss it.'

'What town please, this is Taunton.'

'Taunton??? This is Frome - I'll have to go and put a few lumps of coal on the fire to keep it going till you get here!' and I banged down the phone. I was trembling all over and my insides were churning over. I took a few deep breaths and calmed myself by thinking that the worst of the fire must be over and I had no need to be sarcastic, one central switchboard must control all the stations. My mind became calmer but my stomach certainly did not. I was in no fit state to climb back upstairs to the toilets and then I remembered the old Victorian loo. I knew it was clean and still in working order so I made for it just in time. Fright does terrible things to people, or all those plums I had been eating lately might have upset me.

As I was about to leave the hot dark little closet - I actually had my hand on the latch to lift it up - I had the uncanny sensation that there was someone else in that small suffocating room. What was worse, that someone was making the most rude and fruity noises, admittedly of the kind that could be expected in such a place, but so loud and prolonged! They must have been heard as far as the Beehive! Outraged and frightened I stepped outside, two or three curls of sound followed me out. Pulling myself together I went to see what had happened to Mr Andrews and the fire. Firemen were already arriving, from Frome station, I recognised the captain.

The fire did not cause much damage as far as I could see. It was a pity the American visitors would be greeted by an acrid smell, but there was nothing to be done about it. Flo told me later the cause of the fire was thought to be glass, a pair of spectacles carelessly left, focusing the sun's rays on to an inflammable surface.

I blurted out my tale of the loo and the fireman had a good laugh at my expense. But Mr Andrews, though amused, was quite firm in his opinion that it was not a practical joke, which was the only likely explanation I could think of.

'Have you never heard of our tormented phantom, Mrs Wetherby?' he asked.

'Well, Flo did tell me of a ghost who vanishes through the office partition.'

'Your friend should have finished the story by telling you he also haunts the old loo.'

My youngest son used to work at the building mentioned in this tale and gleefully told me about its resident ghost. I believe people who work there claim to have seen and heard this spook.

GLOBAL VISITS

After working all morning at the shop I spent the afternoon working in the garden, though there I had meant to stay only half-an-hour dead-heading the fuschias. Most gardeners find that once in their gardens one job leads to another, and now it was past tea-time. I straightened my back, decided I must get a little something to eat and started to put away my tools, when I heard the old gentleman across the road calling to me. Would I phone the Gas Board as his mother thought there was something wrong with their stove.

This was done, the Gas Board man reminding me over the phone to switch off the gas at the mains. Wearily I put the phone down and went over the road to see if this had been done. I could not abandon the old gentleman and his mother, who was well over 90, even though it occurred to me they must have looked after each other very well to have reached such advanced ages. When I went in the kitchen the old couple were sitting either side of the cooker, the top of which was blazing merrily.

'My God, switch it off!' I gasped. 'It will blow up or something!'

'Can't switch him off,' said Mr Tucker. 'Tried to, haven't we mother, but he don't work somehow.' He twiddled with a knob just to show me.

'Where do you turn the gas off at the mains?' I tried to keep the hysterical note out of my voice. 'We must be quick!'

'We don't want to switch it *all* off, my dear,' said the old lady calmly. 'The potatoes aren't done yet.'

Getting my terror under control I looked more closely at the cooker, a museum piece if ever I saw one, pre-World War Two. The top was indeed a mass of flames, but burning steadily in order, each burner was alight and flames ran along the pipes. All must have fractured spontaneously.

'Quick, we must all leave the house, let's move!' I darted about agitatedly

ONG–D

looking for a gas tap. 'Do show me where to switch it off!'

'My dear you do be in a bother,' Mrs Tucker smiled at me indulgently. Fearlessly she got up and bent over the stove, moving a pan somewhat gingerly so that she could poke at what was inside. 'Stove's never been the same since Natural Gas,' she complained. 'There, done now George, I reckon. Better turn it off.' Mr Tucker went with agonising slowness to a cupboard in the wall, reached inside and fiddled with a lever. The flames died down and disappeared with a soft plop! plop!

Realising that Mrs Tucker and her son were far more in command than my trembling self, and also in no immediate danger, I went back home leaving them to their supper and the Emergency Gas Board service. I went upstairs to get ready; I would have to forget the snack as I was going out to have supper with my friends. The sight of my bed, plump and comfortable with smooth pillows and the silk quilted coverlet embroidered with pink and peach daisy flowers, was too inviting for my weary frame to resist. I lay down on it, kicking off my shoes and taking off my glasses, promising myself I must not go to sleep - must get ready in a minute to go and meet Clive and Julie. I looked at the clock, I had plenty of time.

My nerves were still jangling from the fright of seeing those flames but gradually I calmed down, soothed by the silence and the beautiful summer evening. The curtains were not drawn, as my bedroom, which faces east at the back of the house, is not overlooked because we are at the top of the hill. I went bang to sleep.

About a quarter of an hour later I opened my eyes and saw through the window a golden star. I studied it thoughtfully then sat up with a start. Some star! It was not yet twilight and I was not wearing my glasses. How could I see anything? I put my glasses on, padded to the window and looked again. There it was high in the sky to the south of Cley Hill, a beautiful gleaming globe, glinting in the slanting rays of the setting sun.

'Might be a balloon,' I thought as I watched the object; I seemed to be compelled to look at it. Suddenly it moved down and was gone. I puzzled about it as I showered and changed, wished I had had my binoculars handy. Balloons are often seen about here, hot air balloons, advertising ones, barrage balloons and those that monitor the weather. My golden globe did not belong to any of these categories. 'Must be a flying saucer,' I decided, 'but who would believe me?'

I met my friends later at the White Hart. They apologised handsomely for keeping me waiting, I had already ordered my meal as I was so hungry I could wait no longer.

'You will never believe us,' said Julie when they were settled, 'but as we were coming away from Warminster we passed about six cars pulled over at the side of the road and people standing by the fence staring at something. Well, you know Clive' - and I did, curiosity always got the better of him - 'We had to stop and get out to see what was going on. We found everybody was watching this large golden ball sitting in the middle of a field about half a mile away. I say ball, but it was bigger than a barn, wasn't it, Clive?'

He nodded, 'Had sort of legs, four cigar-shaped cylinders leaning away from the main body, like this!' Their food had not arrived yet so he was able to set out four little mats in a square on the table with a big ash tray in the middle. 'Well, a bit like that.'

'Tell me more,' I said evenly.

'You don't believe us, do you?' sighed Julie. 'We all said that, no one will believe us. We went on staring at that thing until all of a sudden the small cylinder things began to glow then the whole of it just vanished away. A wind swept over our heads and there was a terrible smell of cabbage.'

'Sort of cooked cabbage, left to go cold.' Clive wrinkled his nose at the memory. 'Wonder if it will come back?'

'Anyway, believe it or not, that is why we were late;' Julie looked me straight in the eye, defying me to disbelieve. 'Almost riveted to the spot we were, once we got out of the car. Mesmerised.'

'Well,' I said, 'I do believe you.' And I told them what I had seen. We agreed we had been watching the same object. Sitting there in the inn with people around and chatter going on we felt reassured and oddly safe. This part of Wiltshire is quite famous for sightings of flying objects but we have never given the matter much thought. I did remember seeing messages chalked on the sides of barns and suchlike buildings when I was out walking along the ridge from Warminster to Westbury. 'Venusians go home, we do not want you here,' and other unfriendly greetings to space travellers.

'There's another thing,' said Clive. 'While we were standing watching, one of the men said he had stopped because his wife had noticed this car at the side of the road and thought the driver was in trouble. They got out and walked back to see if they could help but there was no one in the car. They were puzzled to see the door open - not many people in this day and age leave their cars unlocked, never mind wide open. They looked about and saw this strange golden object and then thought the driver must have gone to take a closer look. They stayed by the hedge and then other people stopped by.'

'When we left,' added Julie, 'there was still a car there empty.'

Clive decided that if it was still there when they drove past home he would inform the police. It was, so he did. There was very little the police could do except shut the door, no law was being broken. They could trace the owner's name and did begin to make enquiries when his wife reported him missing. He lived in Beckington and was last seen that evening when we saw the golden globe. He had gone to see his mother who lived in Warminster and she said he had left to go home about eight o'clock.

We were quite wrong to think nobody would believe us. A few days later when I got home from work Mr Tucker was waiting for me at the gate. 'Got a minute to spare, Miss Nightingale? Mother would like you to see our new cooker.'

All I wanted to do was to put my feet up and have a cup of tea, but my strict upbringing stifled my non-desire to inspect the cooker. 'Give way to age and do what you can to help,' was one of the maxims taught me by my parents. So I went over to the old man's house.

'Gas man said we must have a new one,' Mr Tucker told me as we went up the path, 'so we went down to the showrooms right away and chose. They came this morning to fix it in.'

I must admit I was impressed by the cooker. It must have cost all of £400 and I expect it had been paid for in cash. Besides numerous burners it boasted more gadgets than I knew how to use. On the seamed, flagged floor it stood out like Concorde in a field of bi-planes. The kitchen was not a fitted one; an assortment of cupboards and an old meat safe stood round the walls and in the middle were four upright chairs with cushions and a white pine table made from two planks by Mrs Tucker's father. One end of the table was covered with a clean embroidered cloth on which were stacked the finished-with dinner dishes ready to be washed at the old stone sink.

'There is tea in the pot, sit down and have a cup,' invited Mrs Tucker, well pleased with my awed admiration of her splendid new stove. I loved her tea, always freshly brewed with loose leaves and poured carefully through a strainer into a pretty bone china cup with matching saucer.

'I can spare a minute,' I admitted, and sat down. The cushion on my chair was appliquéd with a red silk cat wearing an enormous tartan bow. Really, it should come as no surprise that the old couple could afford an expensive cooker. They lived well within their means, had done for years; the little money left over accumulating for a long time would mount up.

After expressing the hope that the new stove would cook as well if not better than the old one I began to tell them what I had seen in the sky earlier in the week. 'Did you see it, a huge golden ball, high up in the sky?' They shook their heads.

'I did once though,' offered Mrs Tucker, 'Not this week, a long time ago.'

'Well, don't stop there, my love, tell us more.' I was eager to know, could this be a recurring phenomenon?

'I never heard about this , Mother,' said the old man.

''Twere a long time afore you were born,' his mother told him. 'We were out in the country - yes - we had gone on a Sunday School outing to Southwick, we all went on the old hay cart.' She stopped and thought for a minute. 'It was a lovely picnic,' she sighed and fell silent again. We waited for her to speak, the old man and I. I drank my tea. 'Yes, high in the sky, a big golden ball, all of us children saw it except the little ones, it was evening, see, they were tired, Bessy was asleep with her head in my lap.' I think Bessy was one of Mrs Tucker's sisters. 'I havn't thought about it for years. We were all a bit frightened, didn't know what it was, you see, then the teacher got us singing hymns very loudly and the old horse just plodded on home.' The old lady straightened her pinny, she stared ahead and I knew she did not see her own kitchen, just the ghosts of her childhood. 'Long time ago, I were ten, I think. Time Farmer Doel's son disappeared, his mother came to our mother to ask if we'd seen him that day. Yes, I remember.'

Pleased though I was with Mrs Tucker's memories, Clive and Julie and I had already had ample justification for people believing what we saw. The evening after our meeting at the White Hart there was a very interesting news item in the West Country programme. The television camera crew had gone to photograph a field when a farm worker had reported some strange markings on the growing crop. He was puzzled as to what had flattened the corn so neatly in five separate places. On the screen, for all the viewers to see, there they were, five inexplicable circles, a large one in the middle, four little ones squared round it.

A lady who used to work at the local Spar told all the entranced customers (and I was one of them) how she had seen the flying saucer the day before. My sister swears she once saw a UFO from the window of her flat.

WRONG DESTINATION

My friend Sybilla was a restless soul and completely undomesticated. She disliked staying at home all day and preferred to go visiting or walk about the town looking in shops. She would return home in time to be there when her two little boys came home from school. This particular Tuesday afternoon however she had asked me to call as she needed help in moving some furniture. I was still there when the boys came in. They settled down to play and I was thinking of leaving when the door bell rang and Sybilla with a word of excuse to me went to see who it was.

As I am rather deaf I could not hear enough to identify the visitor, but the boys did, and I was astonished to see them leap to their feet and rush to hide behind the large green sofa. Next minute Sybilla ushered a nun into the room.

'Sister Veronica, this is my friend Annette Westfield,' Sybilla introduced us and then invited the nun to sit down. The sister did not shake my hand but formally bowed her head, said, 'How do you do,' and sat down very upright in her chair. I now understood the boys' swift action; this was their formidable headmistress, a lady renowned for her strict discipline. I would have been a spoilsport to reveal their presence but it amused me to think how pleased Sybilla had been to send James and Timothy to the convent school because she thought they would be taught how to behave.

'Manners are so important,' she remarked, 'especially for boys.'

Sybilla must have forgotten her sons had been in the room, and not by a sound or a movement did they give the game away. Sister Veronica explained the reason for her visit; she had come to ask for help with the convent's annual Sale of Work. My friend readily offered her assistance and I found myself promising to do what I could. I had to get up and go before Sisiter Veronica did, so I never knew how long the boys were left in their uncomfortable position.

OUR NEIGHBOURLY GHOSTS

It is still a mystery to me how Sister Veronica managed to coax a promise of help from me as I had recently decided to be deaf to appeals of this nature. I do not like Sales of Work, though most are for very worthy causes. I went home and gloomily had a look at what was returned from my last efforts to help at my own church's bazaar. There was not much - some sad looking tea cosies and limp oven gloves; my conscience told me I could not offer these to Sister Veronica; they had not sold presumably because nobody wanted them; they were not likely to have more sales appeal on their reappearance.

There was nothing for it, I must buy some more material and make something more up-to-date. I looked round the room for inspiration and my eye fell on the old bead curtain which separated the kitchen from the dining room. These days it did not quite fulfil its purpose - the middle strings were short and ragged as the result of cheerful grandchildren rushing through and tugging them as they passed. The neat geometrical pattern on the curtain had disintegrated and the carefully arranged beads lost their order as one and then another had fallen away from the bottom of the strands.

Must do something about it one day. A fat chunky bead slipped off as I moodily tried to straighten up the lines, and a brilliant idea occurred to me. A large number of the beads were long bamboo tubes but the rest were round seeds, large and small. I could use those to make the weird heavy necklaces young girls seemed so fond of wearing. Painted different colours the beads might be most attractive.

Not one to lose time I had that heavy curtain off its hooks and laid across the table in a jiffy. Briskly I set about stripping it; all the largest beads in one tea cosy, next size in another and so on. The three-inch bamboo tubes I collected up and put aside in a box - the grandchildren could play with those.

My husband came in when I had nearly finished. He looked thoughtfully at the empty doorway and then at the table, not set with the tea things as it should be. Then he came and kissed me.

'I'm so glad you've decided to have a real door there at last,' he said happily. 'The clack of those beads was getting on my nerves.'

'Well, why didn't you say?'

'Oh, I knew, in the fullness of time, you would get tired of it too,' he answered me airily. 'Now, who can we get to put the door in? It will need a proper frame.'

I put the beads away and started to get him something to eat. We discussed matters in the kitchen; inwardly I was so thankful he did not want to do the job himself. I agreed to go out to Nunney and look at some second-hand doors - there is a man out there who specialises in them - instead of buying a new one.

My husband does not like to spend two pennies where one will do.

Next day I was on my way to Nunney thinking how complicated we make our lives. A simple visit to Sybilla had resulted in my being obliged to make large knobbly necklaces and go through the trauma of builders in the house, something bound to disturb my tranquillity. I should have stayed at home and got on planting those tulip bulbs. I could have saved trouble there if I had left them in the ground.

Not many suitable doors were offered for sale but there was one I particularly liked. It had six panels, two sets of three, but the top three were empty, they had not been wood but were originally glazed, lovely shapes like little gothic arches.

'He's old,' said the man carefully as he noticed my interest in this door. 'And pricey, too,' I thought as I allowed him to measure it up for me. With a bit of trimming we decided it would fit my doorway. I flinched when he did tell me the price, but having seen that door I wanted no other.

'I'm afraid I'll have to discuss this with my husband first,' I said, 'but I'll give you a ring this evening and maybe I will collect it tomorrow.' The man offered to deliver it at the weekend when he was free, but as we had a roof rack for the car I could not see any difficulty in fetching it myself and I could not wait till the weekend.

Pondering the best way to tackle my husband and get what I wanted, I set off back to Frome. There was no other traffic on the road, which was odd for a Wednesday, and I began to feel lonely when I noticed ahead of me an old dear walking in the middle of the road. I slowed down and called out 'Going to Frome? want a lift?' I was really going to point out the folly of wandering about in front of cars but changed my mind. Not my place to criticise one of her years.

The old woman turned towards me. She was most peculiarly dressed even for a country woman. Her bonnet - no other word for it - was a wide stiff white frame well over her face, with a pleated piece covering the back of her head and reaching her shoulders. Her dress was long and full and black.

'I am going back to the nunnery,' she said. Her voice sounded rather odd, sort of American. The mention of the nunnery explained things a bit to me, these old nuns did wear old-fashioned habits though I had never seen one in Frome.

'Do get in, I'll take you there,' I offered. As she was still in the middle of the road I turned round and opened the rear door on my side. The old lady peered in and then clambered awkwardly into the car. She sat in the middle of the back seat prodding the upholstery for all the world as if she were testing a sofa before she bought it.

'The door,' I reminded her.

'What is it?' muttered my companion making no move at all to close the door. Wondering if the old lady had anything wrong with her wits I hopped briskly out, shut the door myself, got back in and set off. At least the nuns could be relied on to look after her when I delivered her at the convent. I made a few remarks about the weather but did not fully translate what she said in reply.

'I'll turn left at Badcox and go down Selwood Road' I said brightly as we reached Frome. 'We'll go into the convent the back way.' I spoke more brightly than I felt. I could not understand why I felt so cold and miserable all at once.

'I know where to alight.' The old lady spoke in a very low voice. I felt distinctly uneasy, almost frightened and the palms of my hands were clammy on the wheel. I stopped when I reached Badcox to let some cars go by and then went round to Selwood Road on towards the convent school entrance from which the convent itself could reached. I parked the car over by the gateway which led to the school, got out and opened the rear door.

'Here we are,' I began and then I stopped and looked. There was no one in the car at all. I gave a little shriek of alarm and then opened the door wide to see if the old lady was collapsed on the floor but she was not. Trembling I looked wildly about me and tried hard to collect my thoughts. I got back in the car and sat for a while, then I went home. I told myself I must have been having a very vivid day-dream, it was all Sister Veronica's fault, expecting me to help with her Sale of Work. I did my best to get the whole episode out of my mind, considering as I went about my little household tasks who was the best friend to tell about my experience.

My husband did not argue when I told him about the door and its price - somehow I forgot to mention we would have to get it reglazed - he could see I really wanted it.

'Anything would be better than those dratted beads,' said he. I looked at the beads without enthusiasm, the idea of making necklaces from them no longer held any charm.

The next day I set off to buy the door. I pondered whether to drive there by way of Nunney Catch, but as the area was being ripped up during extensive alterations I decided this would not be sensible. When I saw the door again my spirits revived; this was going to look lovely. Money changed hands and the door was securely lashed to the roof and off I set towards Frome.

Apprehensively I approached the spot where I had seen the nun. When I passed going for the door I had seen nothing but coming back she was there, wandering along just like yesterday. Well, I knew better than to stop this time and I put my foot down.

All at once I saw coming towards me one of those Heath-Robinson farm vehicles, large, noisy and unwieldy; normally they travel quite slowly but this one was going at a fair lick. It seemed to be a long tank on four wheels which leaned outwards from the body and apparently each moved independently of the other. It rattled happily towards the old lady. I was horrified. It would go straight over her. I failed to see that as it was so wide it was coming towards me.

A voice, clear as a bell in my brain, spoke to me. 'Pull over hard left and stop.' I obeyed. The farm contraption lurched past me then came to a halt.

'You all right, Missus?' called out the driver.

'Yes, thank you, not to worry,' I answered. He started up and went on. The road ahead was empty. Does anyone believe in guardian angels anymore? I do, and I thanked mine fervently before I set off again. A thought swam into my mind as I reached Frome. There used to be an old medieval nunnery round Catherine Hill. The old lady probably went from the car yesterday at Badcox; she did not want to go as far as the new convent.

Several years ago, I am told, the Somerset Standard *featured an article about this ghost though I never read it. I have however, heard about the woman who gave a lift to a nun who disappeared.*

A DOG'S CHANCE

We had been walking north-east away from Witham and then had turned south and then west in a circle towards Upton Noble. I was trying hard to ignore the pain from a corn on my littlest toe. The going was pretty rough. Several ditches along the way had been wired across the top of their banks where there should have been stiles; we had been obliged to crawl under the wire - we both had short legs so could not straddle over - then we had to stand up on the slope and jump across to avoid the mud at the bottom of the ditch and next tackle the barbed wire on that side. The ground was everywhere waterlogged and the weather was showery. Taken altogether I began to wonder why I liked walking so much. And now, just as I was breathing heavily after climbing up a hill, we found the field ahead of us full of grazing bullocks.

'I can't run if there is a bull there,' I groaned. 'Can you see one, Lorna?'

'Shouldn't have a bull among this lot,' said Lorna, who had kindly slackened her pace when she realised I was tiring. Lorna is older than I am but a much better walker. She knows the Highway Law inside out,- not just the Motorist's Highway Code - all about the Law of the Land, Rights of Way and Land Owners' Duties and what the County and Parish councils' responsibilities are. With all her scholarship however, Lorna is not particularly fond of cows.

The last field had been a struggle. It had been planted the year before with turnips; where they had been lifted were muddy holes, and where some had been left were little tufty hillocks. There was a right of way over it clearly marked on the map but invisible in fact. We followed the printed route and climbed the stile into the field with the bullocks. There was a gate on the far side, both stile and gate pretty clear indications we were walking along the correct way. I stopped a minute to ease my boot over my corn, wriggling my foot about. The bullocks decided to investigate. First one then another started to amble in our direction. Their pace quickened, and in no time at all seemed to be charging towards us. Lorna ahead of me stood her ground and swished her stick at them, the bullocks happily obeyed her gesture and galloped past us.

'Run for the gate, quick!' ordered Lorna and we both started to trot as fast as we could across the field. With the ground churned up by hooves and with mud clinging to our boots this was not easy. I forgot all about my tiredness and toe as I moved forward heavily but at some speed. Lorna glanced back.

'Oh no, we'll never make it! Hurry!' she yelled. The bullocks, having reached the hedge at the far end of the field, turned round and decided to give us a race, which they won comfortably. Now they were milling about in front of our gate. We abandoned the prescribed footpath and made for the hedge ahead of us, to the right of the gate and the bullocks.

'We'll never get through this,' I panted. Hawthorn is much better than barbed wire at keeping cattle and people in a field.

'Together then,' snapped Lorna. 'We must get to the gate.' So we both swung our sticks in a determined fashion and marched towards the restive bullocks. Obediently they drew back and stood in a perfect semicircle, just at the edge of the swing of the gate. We did not stop to open it, we hurled ourselves over and got daubed in cow muck, though how it settled on us I could not say. We panted and breathed deeply for a minute and then started to laugh.

'Fancy being frightened!'

'Well, they are bigger than us!'

'More of them too!'

Somehow there is nothing like a good fright to put you in a lighthearted mood once you are safely away from the source of fear. I was very proud of Lorna. How had she known just the way to swing her stick?

'Ah well, when I was little, I spent a lot of time on my grandfather's farm, he kept a dairy herd. Never occurred to me to be frightened when he was around.'

Having got our breath back we took another look at the map to make sure of our way and started off again. There was a low wall ahead of us on the edge of a wood. We studied it for a minute, not quite sure of the way in. We were looking for evidences of a stile and did not immediately see it. Then a dog appeared from the wood, he jumped over some tumbled stones and ran away from us. There were the broken wooden uprights of the stile.

'Well, doggie showed us the way,' remarked Lorna, as we set off again. I kept my eyes on the dog, half expecting it to come over and sniff at us - when all of a sudden the dog was not there.

'Wherever did it go?'

'Must have jumped back over the wall,' suggested Lorna uncertainly.

Neither of us had actually seen the dog go. We crossed into the wood wondering whether the dog's owner was about. Everywhere was very still.

'Good Lord,' said Lorna stopping unexpectedly. 'My stick! Bother, I must have left it back there by the gate.'

'Better go back for it,' I said at once. 'Good job we've not come very far.'

'You can wait here,' offered Lorna, knowing how much I disliked retracing my steps. 'I won't be long.'

I shivered, somehow I did not want to wait by myself in that wood. I went back with Lorna. We knew where the stick would be, we had thrown our sticks over the gate to use both hands to haul ourselves over in our flight from the bullocks. We had collected them afterwards, but Lorna had put hers down again when we looked at the map. She retrieved it and we set off again.

As we approached the wood we saw the dog again. He was trotting back alongside the wall where we had first seen him. I looked at him more carefully this time. He was quite a tall dog, thin, black and white short-haired coat, bit like a pointer but with floppier ears, distinctly of mixed lineage. He turned his head towards us. Odd, I thought, his eyes have no life, they are just like two dull black holes. The next minute he was gone. Exactly at the spot where he disappeared before.

'He didn't seem to go over the wall this time,' I remarked drily.

'Perhaps there is a hole there,' said Lorna worriedly, 'Let's go and look.' We hesitated and then decided not to go. We had wasted some time going back for the stick and though the weather was fair at the moment it could turn showery. We still had the best part of three miles to Witham where we had left the car. Besides, I was quite sure there was no hole.

I mentioned the dog next day to Mrs Yarnfield, my neighbour, when I met her by the steps. I knew her husband came from somewhere near Upton Noble.

'Did you ever see a vanishing dog out there?' I asked when I told her where we had been walking. 'Up by the wood beyond the hill?'

'I've never seen such a dog,' she answered, amused by my question. 'I'll ask Mr Yarnfield though.'

I was very fond of this old couple. They had been married nearly 50 years and had spent about 40 of those years in the house next to mine. Mr Yarnfield and I would meet sometimes near the betting shop in Trinity, we both liked to bet though I never placed a bet myself. I'd send one of my grown up sons in the shop to do that, secure in the knowledge that far from teaching them to gamble they would scorn their mother's little weakness and never risk a penny. I am aware not every child would respond like this but I knew my own. I rarely won, and then never more than £6 - caution inhibited me and I never ventured to place more than 50p of the Family Allowance.

The next time I was waiting outside the betting shop Mr Yarnfield called me over, he was sitting on a bench the other side of the road. My middle son came out of the shop with the pink slip which he gave to me with a grin. I thanked him and waved him on home while I went to sit with Mr Yarnfield.

'Did your wife tell you I've been out walking along where you used to live?' I asked.

'She did. Gave me quite a turn,' he answered. 'Talking about the dog. What did he look like?' So I told him all I remembered. Mr Yarnfield looked at me sadly.

'You know,' he said, 'a long time ago, before I were married, I had a dog for eight year, a great one out with the guns. Gypsy feller offered me £10 for that dog but I wouldn't sell. I wouldn't sell. Worth more than money to me that dog.' Indeed I thought he must have been a wonderful dog. £10 was a very handsome sum 50 years ago. 'By my side most of the time that dog,' went on Mr Yarnfield in his deep West Country voice. 'I was working on the farms in those days. But then I had to decide. I was going to be married, see - coming to live in Frome. Couldn't expect a dog like that to live in a town. He were a real dog.' He was silent for a while.

'Er, what did you do then? No one would blame you for selling him ....' At my words Mr Yarnfield stood up and looked at me fiercely.

'No! He were my dog. No one could have him!' He looked up and down the street, took out his handkerchief and wiped his face, or was it his eyes? He sat down. 'I knew what I must do. A week before the wedding I went up to the wood with my dog and my gun. I'd left a spade by the wall and I dug a hole, dog watching me. I told ee to sit and took up the gun. As I shot he looked at me - he knew, oh, he knew! My heart felt as if it were tore out. Then I buried ee.'

He stood up and I stood up and we walked home. We had been sitting in the shade of a huge Victorian warehouse and it was cold. A fat black dog ambled by accompanied by a stout lady. Two terriers sitting in the back of a parked car barked frantically at them as they passed. Mr Yarnfield and I walked by.

'I've never regretted it,' he said. 'When a dog is reared in town I suppose it doesn't matter. But my dog was different. He was always free.'

I thought how much he must have loved his wife.

Woods near Frome are said to be haunted by a dog, though a much fiercer one than the dog in this tale. The earthly fate of the dog in my story is true and was told to me by the owner.

ADMIRING THE VIEW

In front of the imposing gates of the dignified mansion standing to the east of our town there lies a green grass triangle and beyond it a magnificent view, which, I reflected as I set up my easel there, could be appreciated both by those privileged ones inside the gates and those who happened to be outside. The view had long challenged me to paint it.

When I was ready to start, an inexplicable reluctance came over me. I felt shivery and I heard the thump of my heart loud in my ears. Uneasily I stared at the lovely countryside, still and waiting, my eyes drawn to its most dominant feature, a stone age hill fort. I felt something terrible was going to happen. Odd. I wanted to paint but I could not. Minutes passed by as I tried to control this eerie sensation. In the end I put my painting things away, my hands damp and clammy. I hoped I was not going to be ill or faint.

Having a great deal to do I forgot all about not being able to paint as I had hoped, until I was at an exhibition of paintings by local artists, with some very good work by my friends on view. Studying the paintings and sketches I recognised various beauty spots, then it occurred to me that not one of them depicted this view I had wanted to paint. All the time I had lived here, I had never seen it on canvas or paper. Mentioning this to Romany Leadbetter, a fellow artist, he surprised me by recounting his experiences when he had tried to paint the selfsame view. They matched mine exactly.

'Let's go together one day,' I suggested. 'It's hardly likely we'll both feel ill.' He agreed, but with one thing and another we had to wait till our free time coincided. We almost called the whole thing off when he phoned up to tell me of an unusual conversation.

'Remember Samson? Met him the other night in the Cross Keys and told him where we were going to paint. He stared at me horrified, not quite the reaction I expected, so I asked him what was so peculiar and he says that place is haunted.

'Haunted by what?' I wanted to know.

'This monk,' he told me, 'and what is more Samson has seen it with his own eyes. He never goes round that way now but a while back he was driving towards the triangle and he felt the hair on the back of his neck go prickly and he was chilled to the bone. Couldn't understand it so he slowed down. He saw a figure up ahead, standing on the green, thought it was a woman in a long dress at first then he saw it was a monk with a cowl over his head. As Samson went by he turned to look at this fellow - he nearly crashed the car when he saw the monk had no face!' He paused. 'Still want to paint out there?'

I shuddered. 'I never saw anybody. I'll think about it.'

It is hard to understand why we did go in the end. Separately we had been distinctly warned off and now Samson's tale reinforced this taboo. Then I thought about that lovely scenery. I am, in the cold light of reason, of the obstinate opinion that ghosts do not exist. I had largely forgotten my feeling of dread. Samson might have been suffering from flu or something when he saw what he saw, and Romany, well, I've known him for years and noted with a friendly cynicism that whatever I've done he's done better.

I cannot say how Romany came to agree with me but one fine day found us outside the gates of our local stately home preparing to set up our easels. And nothing happened. We went ahead, I looked furtively round for cowled figures and though Romany looked uneasy at first we began to sketch.

It was a glorious June morning, not yet too hot. The sky was a true cerulean blue, misting towards the horizon. I could find no fault with the scenery before me, the rich greens and browns, the subtle shading; how amazingly neat the patchwork lines were, yet I knew that, close to, the hedges were as straggly as tangled wool. We sat there happily. Once I started I could concentrate, but the beginning was a hurdle. Romany settled down first, then with a sigh I took up my brush.

For about 20 minutes we painted in peace. The birds' song, little twitching noises in the grass, the rustle of leaves; all these delightful sounds soothed and inspired us. Little by little I became aware of another sound, a rushing thumping throb in my ears. It took me a minute to realise it was my own heartbeat. I was fast in the grip of a mounting terror. In the air was a stillness, a horrible foreboding. I had been limning in the hillfort commanding the view; a bright blaze of light shone from the hill, then two more.

'Almost as if someone is signalling,' muttered Romany. I had forgotten all about him; with a start I looked at him and saw he was suffering from the same shocking sensations as I. I felt walled in an iceberg, I wanted to run but I could not move. I managed to grasp Romany's hand; my teeth started to chatter.

'Let's go, I can't stand this.'

We put our things together, dropping tubes of paint and scattering brushes. I bent down to pick them up, straightened my back and tried to stagger towards the car. I had gone a few steps when I heard right behind me the most awful groaning sigh, utter desperation and hopelessness in one evil sound! I screamed and ran to the car. Romany, who was in front, looked back and his eyes bulged in terror. 'My God, it's the monk!'

Once in the car we flung our gear on the back seat and Romany tried to start the car fumbling with his keys. In a state of near hysteria I willed myself to breath deeply.

'We are safe now,' I stuttered. 'Just wait, wait. You can't drive in a panic.' We sat for a minute before Romany calmed himself and started the car. We dared not look back.

At my place we discussed the affair and tried to rationalise things.

'I'm not going back there ever,' I said flatly. 'I am not.'

Romany gave a weak grin. 'Oh, what's happened to the "There's no such thing as ghosts" attitude' that I know and love? Where is your fighting spirit? Your backbone?'

'Shattered into little pieces! I could not look! What frightened you most, Romany?'

'It was the voice of the ghost, the hopeless groan it gave. Seemed to claw at my guts.'

'I heard it too,' I said. 'There was unbearable agony concentrated in that sound, almost as if its mind was giving way.'

'I wonder,' Romany spoke thoughtfully, 'remember those flashes of light? I think we were seeing what he saw, only he knew what they meant.'

'Signals, do you think? Was morse invented in monkish times?'

'I don't think so, anyway there were only three uneven flashes. More like the sun glinting on something. One thing, I'll never disbelieve a ghost story again. '

For weeks afterwards we recounted our grisly meeting to all our friends, who, interested at first, became understandably bored. I decided to forget the whole thing. My friend Elsie urged me to get out more and invited me on an outing to Bratton with our favourite society. We were to be taken round the village by a famous historian who had made her home there.

Bratton was lovely and the historian exactly my idea of an ideal guide, someone of vast knowledge who could impart to others both facts and enthusiasm. She was dressed in sensible shoes and a blue and white checked frock, on her head was a straw hat, coolie type only larger. I instantly broke the tenth commandment and coveted the dress; I wished I knew where she bought it. She carried rolled up a gentleman's large black umbrella, useful in case of showers, but it was used to point out things and to make sweeping gestures of emphasis. It came into great play when, after a comprehensive tour of the village, she was describing the savage battles between the Christian English commanded by Alfred and the pagan Danes. Both sides were prepared to fight to the death, no quarter given in the bitter struggle waged on the heights above Bratton. Indeed gruesome evidence had come to light during recent excavations when skeletons of men identified as Danes had been found buried in a mound, all with their hands tied behind their backs.

'England stayed Christian because Alfred defeated the Danes,' stated our guide; and a piece of history taught to me in childhood flared into reality as I stared at the stark lonely hills above the village. We were tired now and eagerly accepted our guide's invitation to sit in her house and garden (there were about 30 of us) to have our tea which we had thoughtfully been instructed beforehand to bring with us. Her kindness was truly appreciated.

The cottage and garden were at the top of a slope, a buttress wall held them to the hillside. Elsie and I sat on a stone seat in the garden, and as my eyes studied the little lawn, the shape reminded me of another green, and with a shudder I was back with the problem of trying to forget my ghostly experience.

Impulsively I jumped up and went to look for our hostess. She was sitting in a beautiful old chair - all her furniture was beautiful in its own right though nothing exactly matched - and had finished showing a few of her cherished manuscripts to some of our party. I wanted to know whether there were any monks around in the time of Alfred. I was pretty sure there must have been, but someone else cornered her attention so I turned aside to look at the manuscripts and I never did ask her.

The niggle in my mind grew. The English and the Danes fought all over that part of Wiltshire not just at Bratton, though the battle there may have been the decisive one. I told Romany about it as we were sitting on the top of Cley Hill. You can see miles over the countryside up there, it gives me a most satisfying sensation of being in command. Now my head was buzzing with the sound of long forgotten battles fought over a thousand years ago.

'Why do you think our ghost should be connected with Alfred?' asked Romany. 'He is just as likely to have been any old monk who liked to sneak away after matins and admire the view.'

'I don't know why,' I answered, 'it bothers me to think of that ghost riveted in one place in an absolute agony of mind all these centuries and nobody has done anything to help.'

'He won't let us do anything,' commented Romany, 'you can't even sketch on the green - up he comes and frightens you to death.'

'He might be trying to tell us something,' I said.

'Well, he's going the wrong way about it, nobody's got the courage to go there again, certainly not me..'

A party of hikers came over the brow of the hill, two big men in shirts, shorts and knee length socks and a woman in a kind of a sack. They all wore heavy walking shoes and carried knapsacks. One of the men also carried a folded-up tripod with brass bound legs, the sort used for telescopes or cameras. We nodded to each other companionably, they tramped on by and we watched in silence. As they climbed down, the sun caught the brass and rays of light shone into our eyes, making us blink.

I gasped. 'We saw shafts of light like that from the gates. That's what the monk could see.'

'Hikers? said Romany sceptically.

'No of course not! He saw an army on the march, they carry spears and things of shiny metal. He would be desperately afraid, he could not fight because of his vows. It might have been the Danes.'

'Could have been Alfred's army,' suggested Romany.

'So? He knew there was going to be a battle,' I argued. 'He couldn't do anything, he was terrified.'

'Calm down,' said Romany. 'You are no historian, you are letting your imagination run away with you.'

Sitting up there in the sun I could imagine anything. We got up slowly to walk back down and invented all sorts of reasons for the monk's haunting.

But one thing is certain, he is still there.

A taxi-driver taking me from Bath to Frome in his cab told me how he had seen this ghostly monk and how every time he thought about it the hairs on the back of his neck stood up. He vowed he would never drive past that spot again.

UNTIMELY INFLUENCES

Marguerite was a truthful child.

'You've put too much sugar in this apple pie, Mummy,' was her verdict on the pudding at Sunday's lunch.

'The door does not fit,' she told my husband when he had worked all day making a little cupboard for her toys. As indeed it did not.

'Why do I have to wear shabby clothes?' she asked loudly in church one day when, yes, she had been dressed in a not new outfit which needed the hem adjusting.

Little remarks like these made my husband and me feel that we were being weighed in the balance and found wanting; as parents we agreed it was difficult to teach Marguerite tact. If she grew up finding fault as accurately as she did now, her outspoken ways would certainly arouse antagonism in those around her. Why, we loved her dearly, we were proud of her, but to be constantly found fault with did not make for a trouble-free relationship. We were bothered about how she would fare in the world later on.

We live in a house and a cottage joined together, surrounded by a lovely garden. The stone walls are thick and solid. On a stormy day, safe inside them, you cannot hear the wind outside; though on the debit side I have to go down on my knees and pray for the centuries-old roof, which is badly in need of repair.

Emma, our other daughter, is as sensitive to people's feelings as Marguerite is insensitive. No word of criticism passes her lips. When my sister came to stay, Emma begged me not to mention that she was sleeping in Marguerite's room. I was puzzled, we had several people staying at the time, beds were in short supply, it seemed simple to move the girls together. But Emma thought my sister would be embarrassed to think she had obliged the child to move, so I never mentioned the matter.

The thorn in our flesh is the dog Bonzo, half collie, half pointer. He loves Marguerite but unfortunately barely tolerates anybody else. He does have an affection for our rabbit, and, if not watched, will nudge open the latch on the hutch, much to the delight of the rabbit, who will promptly push the door wide and hop down into the garden, heading straight for my husband's vegetable patch. When gorged he hides under the gooseberry bushes, making capture difficult. We have to wait till Marguerite comes home from school as the rabbit will come to her when she calls his name.

One autumn, when Marguerite was about eight, we noticed a change in her manner. She did not comment so often on our shortcomings, and overnight her untidy room seemed to straighten itself out. She held her tongue when the curry was too hot or too mild and even fetched a needle and cotton to sew a button on her coat. Delighted at first at these signs of maturity, I began to worry. The child did not talk to us as much; she was quieter, more submissive.

One day Marguerite went into the garden to harvest the apples. She went unasked: normally I had to beg the children to help with this task. I was watching from the window, something seemed not quite right, was she talking to someone? The dog was not with her. I became aware of another person standing beyond Marguerite and the little apple tree. I opened the window to see better. It must have been a trick of the shadows, there was a woman standing there, in a long, wide, dark red dress. Even from that distance I noticed her long white fingers spread out like a fan and a high ruff-like collar round her throat.

I blinked, decided I was worrying too much about my little daughter, though I would go and see her teacher at school. I reflected she would not come across many parents who were worried by the good behaviour of their child.

Miss Pritchard had noticed the improvement in Marguerite. 'I'm so pleased,' she said. 'She was, well, not disruptive, of course, but such a giggler! Now she is as good as gold. She wrote a lovely little piece the other day: I asked them to draw and describe someone they knew. Look how neat it is compared with the work she was doing some months ago.' She showed me the piece. 'Marguerite chose someone quite formidable, her granny perhaps?'

I was intrigued. Marguerite does not know her grandmothers, my mother died before she was born and mother-in-law lives in America. I read the piece and hid my dismay as I handed it back.

'Marguerite's imagination must have been working overtime. I am sure she knows no one who would fit this description.'

But I was not sure. My daughter had drawn the shadow in the garden, exactly what I had seen: a lady in a long dress, wide over the hips, the bodice coming to a point over the stomach. The head was set on a row of squiggles which I took to be a ruff. Respect for this lady came out strongly in the simple, childish words written beside the drawing.

I walked home, trying to analyse my distinctly resentful feelings. My husband and I had not tried to alter Marguerite in any conscious way; her forthrightness had been irritating but very often justified. As for her untidiness, well, I can remember what I was like as a child, and I suppose we could be blamed for giving the children so many things to cope with. She had changed, though, and now I found it was from no planned effort on Miss Pritchard's part. I thought about the little essay and shivered. Literally, a shadow had fallen between me and Marguerite.

'Your teacher showed me your school work today, Margie,' I said at teatime. 'But whoever was the lady in the long dress?'

'She comes into the garden sometimes, Mummy, I first met her in the bathroom. I thought she was a friend of yours.'

I gasped. 'Margie, you are making this up.' Then I thought, why did I say that? After all, I recognised the description.

'No I'm not, Mummy,' Marguerite was shocked. 'She is your friend. She keeps telling me I must obey you and be good, oh, all sorts of things. She had a little girl once. I never make things up.'

'She can't make things up,' put in Emma, who could.

'Have you ever seen this lady, Emma? Does she speak to you?'

Emma shook her head. 'Margie told me about her but when I went to see her she never came. I wanted to ask why she sat in the bath, we never sit in the bath with our clothes on.'

'Why didn't you tell me?' I wanted to know.

'I thought you knew,' answered Marguerite, surprised. 'Lots of strange people come here to stay, she didn't seem any different.'

'I expect she likes Margie better than me because she's got fair hair just like her little girl,' said Emma gloomily.

'She doesn't like Bonzo, I shut him up in the lobby if I see her in the garden. He kind of yelps, as if he's frightened,' added Marguerite. The children went on calmly eating their tea, completely unaware of the turmoil I was feeling.

'How long had this been going on?' I asked bleakly. Quite clearly I was failing my child as a mother.

Marguerite thought for a moment. 'I don't know, but she first came when the light in the bathroom broke and you had forgotten to buy a new one so we were using candles and torches. I was cleaning my teeth, you came in and I said, 'You ought to remember to buy the things we need,' but it wasn't you, it was this lady. She said I must not censure my mother. I didn't know what she meant, but she explained.'

'Weren't you frightened? Why didn't you call me?'

'Why should I be frightened ' Marguerite paused, then said, 'If you don't know her, Mummy, I'll tell you next time she comes. I expect you'll remember her when you see her.'

'What's her name?' Everybody has a name.

'Dame Tassell. Can we go now?' and I let them leave the table, while I poured myself out another cup of tea and tried to make sense of what I had heard. As my husband is easily irritated if I talk to him about what he calls 'fanciful imaginings', I could not confide in him till I had something more concrete to tell him.

I waited in some anxiety to see what happened next. A few days later Marguerite came in from the garden. 'Dame Tassell is here, Mummy. Do you want to speak to her?'

I glanced through the window and there by the apple tree was the lady. I could see her so clearly. She wore a neat headress sewn with pearls, and her face was severe and thin. I grew ice cold and I could feel the muscles along the back of my neck tighten. I stepped into the garden, Marguerite ahead of me, but there was no one there! I could see nothing by the apple tree! Marguerite saw someone, I heard her say, 'This is my mother, Dame Tassell,' in a confident voice. I began to shake, we were both quite mad. Turning away I went back to the house.

Marguerite came after me. 'Why don't you speak to her, Mummy? She's your friend, I like her.' I was trembling and my head began to throb. How could you explain to an eight-year-old child that she was seeing a ghost? I kept a tight grip on my temper and smothered the jealous feeling that the child was taking more notice of the ghost than of me.

All that evening and during the night and the next day my headache grew and swelled. I took some tablets, but it was still there heavy and sullen though the pain subsided. When the girls came home I told Marguerite she must not speak to Dame Tassell any more. She looked so sad I relented a little and said she could say goodbye.

'Tell her you must obey your mother's wishes,' I said craftily. Emma offered to go with her sister, I had thought of going myself but could not face the eerie feeling of talking to nothing. The girls went into the garden, then Marguerite came back to tie up Bonzo. The hair on the dog's neck was standing up; he was not long-haired, though his mother had been a collie. A broad white band was marked round his neck, it looked very handsome against his black and white coat.

I stared through the window and saw the ghost lady walking up and down by the apple-tree. Emma sat on a bench by the wall, I could see she had no idea anyone else was by; she was swinging her feet and touching the lady's long skirts as she swished by, but neither took notice of the other.

Marguerite, with Bonzo safely tied up, went out into the garden, giving me a reproachful look as she passed. At that moment the pain in my head burst through the drugs and a fierce burning throb began to nag at my whole being. A vicious thought entered my besieged brain. So the lady did not like Bonzo, and why not? *I* allowed the dog's companionship; that dog would have protected Marguerite to the death if need be.

Quite deliberately I went to the lobby and set Bonzo free from his leash. He jerked away from me and made for the garden. Too late I noticed his wide terrified eyes. I had a sense of impending disaster and reached out to tie him up again but he evaded my grasp and bolted off to the garden. He stopped for a moment when he got outside, panting, then he walked forward, stiff-legged. He was as terrified of the ghost as I was. I called out a warning and frozen with horror watched through the window.

Marguerite reached out a hand to pacify the dog, patted him and spoke to him soothingly. The lady, frightened, backed away. That was enough for the dog, he knew he was her master; with a growl and a snarl he advanced, his eyes still wild and rolling. The ghost, moving back, reached down to gather her full skirts in her hands. I saw she had reached the bench where Emma sat, gazing at her sister and the dog with bewildered amazement. Realising I must do something I got the strength to go into the garden but too late! Even as Marguerite tried to pull the dog back by his collar he lunged forward, snapping. But his jaws sank into the real child, not the ghost who did not belong to his time, and Emma's leg was red with blood. Then the dog shrank away, cowed by our screams. Emma was whimpering with pain and shock, I gathered her in my arms and saw with relief the gash was not too deep. Aghast at my wickedness I took her to hospital; after a few stitches and an injection she was allowed home.

My husband's decision was immediate and the dog was taken to be put down. No pleadings moved him, he was deaf to the children's tale of how he got loose and my own incoherent claim to be responsible. Later I was silent and Marguerite never found out that I was to blame. I had got rid of the ghost, she never came again. The life of the dog was a monstrous price to pay.

The parents of the child who saw the Elizabethan lady sitting in the bath subsequently found, during alterations to the bathroom, the remains of a fireplace where the bath was. So the lady, back in her own time, was presumably sitting by the fire.

LOVE IN A TIME WARP

Mother's attitude irritated me. What is wrong with living in a brand new house on a new estate on the outskirts of a market town? Yet in conversation with her friends who came over to tea Mother seemed compelled to offer explanations.

'Well, I tried for a year after Geoffrey died, but in the end I just had to give up our lovely house in Bath. The rates were positively extortionate and the cost of repairs - my dear! - I simply had to sell and move to something less expensive, my income won't grow to keep pace with inflation!'

Her friends already knew all this and thought her solution sensible, so why did she harp on it so? I was on my way home from college where I was studying for a degree in psychology and the thought of hearing Mother going on and on about coming down in the world depressed me. It was dreadful when Father died, I suffered too, but she had her health and strength and enough to eat and the house was crammed with expensive furniture - she could always sell that if her income dwindled so much - why be negative?

Perhaps she wasn't. Perhaps when I got home she would be back to her old self, helping with this charity and that, dishing up Meals on Wheels and visiting housebound folk. In the old days it did not take much to make Mother happy.

I was not happy myself at the moment as my happiness was bound up with a certain person. Just thinking about Alan's dark blue eyes and the way his hair grew and his strong hands made me melt inside. I had come to terms with the fact I did not have the same effect on him. He had bought himself one of these student tickets for £99 with which you can travel anywhere on the continent for a month - a whole month! I could not live a month without him, and he thought nothing of leaving me! Gloomsville stretched ahead complete with a moaning mother.

Reaching home I deliberately stifled my irritation and my unhappiness - must make the best of things. I knocked on the door and looked about me, at the houses of dark brown brick, the neat trim gardens, why, someone across the walkway had planted two flourishing yuccas which gave a positively exotic look to the place. We had planted hydrangea bushes and rose trees and set out rows of bedding plants. That reminded me, I stepped over to see what colour the hydrangeas were. They were not blue, as I hoped, but a delicate shade of pink. Ah well, must be the wrong soil.

Mother had opened the door and was looking round for me. 'Carrie darling! You're back! My lovely baby!' and she hugged and kissed me. I let her go on; after all she had only me now and it made her happy. I did not tell her about Alan, there was nothing to tell.

A vacancy for a part-time job as a waitress in a rather posh hotel near us was advertised and I applied. At first the proprietor looked at me dubiously; I realised why and could have kicked myself. I was wearing my usual gear, I like to wear long skirts and embroidered cotton blouses and I top them with this super jacket I picked up at a jumble sale. It is the most lovely combination of tangerine and yellow flowers on a cream ground with green leaves and blue butterflies. Mother does not like it, it is too old and threadbare round the cuffs to please her, and obviously the manager of the hotel had the same quaint hang-ups. Luckily two other students who applied were wearing jeans and leather jackets and he didn't like them either. I was saved by his secretary who was the daughter of a friend of Mother's; she came in while I was there and had a few kind words. I explained I did have more suitable clothes, so he decided I could be trusted and gave me the job.

I was glad to be occupied as day after day went by without a word, not a letter or card from Alan. He had given me no address so I could not phone or write. Then Mother began to behave oddly. I would find things in my room moved about and the bedside lamp would be switched on at night. Why she wanted to look in on me during the night I could not fathom. I became so depressed I had to speak out.

'Mother, why do you fiddle with my things? I don't go into your room and rearrange it.'

Mother looked at me oddly. 'Whatever do you mean, Carrie? I wouldn't touch anything of yours, you know I never have.' And that was true. But when I went into my room I found my lovely cuddly panda bear that Dad had given me when I was four face down on the floor instead of in his place where he always was, sitting in my bedside chair.

The next day when I got home and went to my room the first thing that met my gaze was the odd appearance of the bookcase. The books were still on the shelves neatly side by side but every single one was back to front, the spines at the back, the open end facing the room. Furious, I tackled Mother at once, asking her to come up and see for herself.

'Now, Mum, whatever possessed you? Look -' and I pointed. Mother sat down suddenly on the bed.

'Carrie, I didn't touch your books. Come down and have your tea.' She got up and quietly left the room.

'Who did then? I didn't. You are being silly,' I called after her. I could not accuse her of lying outright. I began to think, she has cracked up, she did not want to move away from Bath, her mental state must need help. Slowly I took out each book and turned it round. I got the oddest feeling I was being watched, but Mother was already downstairs in the kitchen, I could hear her setting out crockery. I joined her, we did not speak much. She did not offer any explanation and I was trying to nerve myself to suggest she visit a doctor.

Next morning I woke up early. It was full dawn, sunlight was streaming through the window. I had the same sensation of being watched. I turned over onto my back and there, sitting on the end of my bed, was a Roman soldier! He had dark curly hair and was wearing a breastplate over a linen tunic and one of those distinctive skirts made of strips.

I was not a bit afraid, I suppose I thought I was dreaming. He was young and vigorous, I noticed the strong muscles on his arms and the breadth of his shoulders. He was tanned, and when I looked into his dark eyes I just knew he was my friend. He started to smile, but then I saw him slowly vanish, I was staring at him no longer but through him and then at the picture on the wall.

I did not get up. I lay in bed going over every detail I could remember. I had felt the bedclothes tight over my feet; when he disappeared the weight lifted away. He could not be a ghost! He was so real, I wanted him to come back.

When Mother came in with a cup of tea I said simply 'Mum, I've just seen a Roman soldier.' She sighed and said, 'I knew you would find out one day that this house is haunted.'

'Well,' I grinned, 'at least that solves my problem, I was going to ask you to see a psychiatrist, looks like we'll both have to go.' We laughed together.

'Are you afraid , Carrie? I was going to change rooms - move all your things out, because the odd things happen only here, but then I thought I had better ask you first.'

'You have seen him then, Mother?' I asked eagerly. I wanted to hear all I could about my handsome soldier, but no, she had not seen him. She had felt a presence and noticed how things were misplaced.

ONG-F

I did not tell anybody else about my soldier, it was enough that Mother knew. From that day onward I stopped looking for mail from Alan and never gave him a thought. I spent hours in my room, waiting for the soldier to come back.

And he did. This time we tried to talk, which was not easy; at first I couldn't understand a word he said, then I realised he must be talking Latin. He did not understand me. I listened carefully, my half-remembered schoolgirl Latin woefully inadequate. Still, there existed between us a wonderful feeling of belonging, and patiently we made ourselves understood.

His name was Roscius Gaius Valerian Patroculus. I called him Roscio and he called me Cara. It took me several meetings to realise he had no idea that I belonged to the twentieth century; I was not a ghost to him. My Latin was far too primitive to make him understand our plight. He lived in soldiers' quarters and I was an elusive young girl who came and went.

Then my everyday life with Mother and at the hotel became the dream and my life with Roscio the reality. I was in love, 20 years old and truly in love for the first time, and he loved me. We knew it before we put it into words. Sometimes, when he was gone and I was alone commonsense would urge me to be practical. I was usually so sensible, and here I was wasting my time dreaming about a ghost soldier who lived 1,700 years ago - 1,700 long years, my girl! But I could not come out of my dream.

One day he told me he would be gone a half-day's march; if I wanted to see him I must ride there. I stared at him trying to translate his words, to understand where he was going. I knew he wanted me to follow him. His fellow soldiers told him his 'Celtic maid' was teasing him; once he was gone he would be forgotten. I did have black wavy hair and blue eyes, but had never thought of myself as a Celt.

Then he was gone. I waited four days, I remembered I had not asked him when he would be back. I grew desperate. I was so absent-minded I had to give in my notice at the hotel, customers were annoyed at my clumsiness. I studied an old map of the region and the ancient Roman Fosseway stood out clearly. A half-day's march from Frome, would that be Bath? I clearly got the impression that Roscio was talking about a small unimportant place; Bath was well known to the Romans. Could be anywhere; I looked along the Fosse, there was Radstock not so far away.

I rode there on four wheels, courtesy of the Bristol Omnibus Company. I knew I would have to get a taxi back, for buses stopped running between the country towns after six. This part of the Fosseway is buried under Radstock's roads, covered in tarmac and pavement, but it is still a footpath where it runs in from Stratton. The way was steep, I climbed up slowly away from the town. I was breathless with anxiety, was this the right place? I stumbled now and again, brambles caught in my hair.

He was there. I could see him standing at the top, where the path flattened out. My heart swelled with relief and I cried out with joy. He ran lightly down to meet me, to take me in his arms. He was real and vital and we were together.

I went again the next day. How those hours flew! I can remember every detail of the countryside, the individual leaves and twigs of the bushes beside us and the blades of grass and the wild flowers, Stratton straight ahead framed in a distant clump of trees. I felt so complete and content.

Before I left him he said abruptly, 'Will you wait for me?' I promised I would wait, not knowing what I meant. To be close to him was the only thing I wanted in my whole life.

When I came again he did not come. Another day I went back, still he did not come. I went again, and again I waited. Once a walker passing me by stopped and said, 'Can I help you, my love? You look so unhappy, are you ill?' She was a dear old soul, dressed in flat shoes, thick tweed skirt and shapeless cardigan. She had a kind, wise face. I thanked her and shook my head, I could not put into words the torment in my mind that Roscio would think I had betrayed him. I must have looked peculiar, waiting up there night after night, my long skirts and my hair blowing in the wind. In the end I knew he would not come.

I had no consolation. All I could do was sit in my room thinking over what he had said, how he looked when he said it. Into my anguished thoughts crept a cold little voice, 'You fool, you live in the Atomic Age, men alive now have been to the moon! Roscio is a dead man, a ghost.' But I will remember and love that ghost all my life and I will see him again.

Oh, Alan came to see me before the holidays were over. He and Mother got on famously, she thought he would cheer me up. He told us about the wonderful friends he had made, the marvellous sights he had seen. I felt a million years old.

When I was working in the Oxfam shop one day my partner told me her neighbour's daughter had seen a Roman soldier sitting on the end of her bed, 'he vanished slowly, like mist.'

IN NEED OF A BUTLER

'What do you think of my new chair?' asked Mrs Saunders. Mother looked at it and considered. The two ladies were in Mrs Saunders' sitting room having morning coffee and a pleasant chat.

'A very handsome piece of furniture, though, if you don't mind my saying so, dear,' - Mother did not want to hurt our neighbour's feelings - 'it doesn't quite fit in. I feel it's built on a larger scale.'

Mrs Saunders sighed. 'That's what I think myself.'

The chair, a recent purchase but decidedly not new, had a heavy wooden frame; the arms had been carved economically but the backrest was surmounted by a huge scallop shell; the broad cushioned seat was high, supported on straight sturdy legs, the front pair complete with castors. It was indeed out of place with the rest of the room which was furnished in a contemporary style, low chairs and sofas upholstered in tweed, with plain varnished woodwork; the television was set on spindly legs and there was a modern bookcase-cum-divider holding a streamlined collection of ornaments.

Mother went to sit in the alien chair.

'It's very comfortable,' she remarked. 'But why ever did you buy it? I thought you were happy with the way this room looks.'

'I need a high one for my mother-in-law,' explained Mrs Saunders. 'Now she is suffering from that hip complaint, she finds sitting in a low chair can be uncomfortable, and once she has been sitting down any length of time it's hard for her to stand up. I saw this one in a second-hand shop, only five pounds, and it looked just what I wanted till I got it in place. They won't take it back either,' she added ruefully.

'Only five pounds?' gasped Mother, 'for all that lovely carving? My dear, I'll take it off your hands, we'll find room for it.'

And Mother did. When my brother Steve and I got home from school we found the furniture in the dining room had been rearranged to accommodate the chair. The dog had already taken a fancy to it. After leaping at us and licking us all over in his usual welcoming fashion he settled back on to its broad seat. We turfed him off to try out its bouncing potential. Steve sat in it first and said irreverently he felt like God. Mother was shocked, but when I tried it out I saw what he meant, the high enveloping seat felt like a throne commanding a lofty view.

'It's not quite right,' said Mother. 'I've got some material left over from making the curtains. When I've recovered it, then it will fit in.'

My heart sank, remembering the last time Mother had tackled home upholstery. She had attempted to renew a sofa; for weeks the place was smothered in tacks and horsehair and a horrible dark grey flocking. Even when the mess was cleared up the dog found a loose end in the finished work and in no time at all the 'new' sofa was saggy again.

'Don't you think you could manage without taking it to bits? I coaxed. 'Just sort of stretch the material over and nail it in place - look, I'll help.'

'Be done much quicker,' agreed Mother, and we set to work. Father approved of the additional chair, but my brother did not.

'One more bit of junk,' he said gloomily. I was not surprised, his ideal home was his best friend Poggy's, brand spanking new from front door to back and stuffed with the most amazing electrical gadgets, things like electric tooth-brushes and massagers and skirting boards which would lift at the touch of a switch and whisk away all the dust on the floor. When his parents were away, Poggy's playmates used to enjoy trying out all this fascinating equipment; Steve said it was almost as good as Space Invaders.

The two of us were sitting in the dining room one evening, doing our homework more or less, when I heard Steve gasp in amazement. He was staring fixedly at the chair. I glanced round but saw nothing out of the way, except that the dog was curled up underneath.

'What's the matter?'

'Can't you see, Sis' he said in a whisper.

He did not reply, just stared ahead intently. I waited. Then he sighed. 'Must have been seeing things, I could have sworn there was an old gentleman sitting in that chair, a fat old man with a chain across his middle and a blue stripey waistcoat.'

'Well, Meg didn't seem to mind. I thought dogs didn't like ghosts.'

'Sis, he was stroking the dog.'

It was my turn to gasp, for indeed now I remembered the dog's ears had seemed to lie freakishly flat against his head, as if they were being smoothed. We looked at each other for a minute and then both jumped up and ran to tell Mother.'

'Bunkum!' she said flatly, 'Go back and finish your homework. What a ridiculous excuse. I'll come and sit in the chair.'

Mother refused to listen to our excited explanations so we meekly returned to our work and never mentioned our experiences to her again.

For Steve saw the ghost more than once; he got accustomed to seeing him regularly, but he assured me he was not afraid any more.

'He's a nice old fellow,' he told me. 'Just sits there happily, does no harm. He's very fat, he can't move easily. What's more I've an idea that chair was made specially for him. He's fond of dogs, Meg knows that. Poggy wants to come and see him.'

I smiled to myself hearing the pride in his voice. At last! Steve had something Poggy had not. But when he came Poggy did not see our friendly ghost and disbelieved the whole tale.

'Why don't you ask the old gentleman to do something, give Poggy proof that he's there?' I suggested. I firmly believed in our ghost, especially when I saw Meg lying under the chair wagging her tail for no reason at all.

'We don't speak to each other,' explained Steve. 'He doesn't want to bother us. But I could try, I suppose.'

That evening, however, Father came home with the news that his firm had promoted him. The need for establishing some sort of supremacy over Poggy and his worldly goods would soon be a thing of the past, for this meant that we would have to move nearer London. The house was immediately put up for sale and assumed an unnatural neatness. We children were urged to help so we enthusiastically stuffed everything out of sight into cupboards and drawers and kept mostly out of the way of prospective buyers, though we reserved the right to inspect them at a distance, unobtrusively.

Life at home grew more and more uncomfortable. It was terrible when the dinner was not ready and my school blouse was not ironed, but we had to put up with it. We tried doing things for ourselves, but we only got in Mother's way, though she stayed cheerful about it all.

The day came when, the house still not sold, Father decided he must go on ahead, he must move alone into our new house, for travelling to and fro had become expensive. Besides, he intended to supervise several necessary repairs that had to be done, so that when we all settled in together our family life could straightaway resume its tranquil flow.

I noticed Mother continually wore trousers once Father had departed. We gave up being tidy, to my relief - it was irritating not being able to find anything; the muddle we usually had around was in its way much more organised. Mother became generally more protective towards Steve and me. She had given up most of her activities once the For Sale notice had been erected outside the house - she was afraid to miss a single person who might be interested in buying - she still however called on Mrs Saunders; as her house was across the street Mother could keep an eye on anyone going up our garden path, though not a very satisfactory arrangement for Mrs Saunders I would have thought, to have Mother staring out of the window instead of attending to the conversation.

Eventually a letter arrived from the estate agent, we had a prospective buyer who had made a firm offer for our property. Accordingly our solicitors were instruted to go ahead with the sale. We wanted to know which of the people who had tramped over our house wanted to buy it. Mother said it was a Mr and Mrs McEvoy, and as she could not remember them she decided they must have been the people Father had shown round when she had gone alone to the Parents' Evening at school. Steve and I could not place them, we did not know names - we wanted a description.

'Well, you shall see them,' said Mother one morning, 'I've received a very nice letter from the lady, they both want to come round to measure up for curtains.'

'She'll come when we're at school,' I complained, but Mother said this was not likely. She got in touch by phone and found the most convenient time was the next evening. I rushed home from school, anxious not to miss them. Steve dawdled along, calling after me as I rushed by, 'They won't come before they've had their tea,' and he was right.

We sat waiting. I hoped fervently our nice house was not going to be sold to the disagreeable couple who said what a poky little kitchen and how did we manage without a hatch. Mother's face had been a study in outraged pride, she thought they had said 'hutch' and were likening us to rabbits. Steve said he hoped they were not the ones who had laughed aloud at the squat feet on our ancient bath.

When the McEvoys did arrive we were relieved to find they were none of these, in fact we had never seen them at all. Mrs McEvoy was older than Mother, plump with red hair; she wore a brown and yellow tweed skirt and a quilted anorak. Mr McEvoy looked younger than Father, he was on the portly side too and his anorak matched his wife's.

Mother ushered them in, offered them tea and then asked did they just want to measure the windows or would they like to see over the house once more. They were keen to see the whole place again, very well pleased with what they saw to be their property. Mr McEvoy took the measurements for the curtains first and his wife noted them down. Then they spent an agreeable half hour inspecting the house. Just before they left, Mrs McEvoy turned to Mother and asked, 'By the way, how is the elderly gentleman? Did he enjoy the fancy dress ball?'

Mother stiffened, she had never considered Father to be elderly. 'My husband is in quite good health, thank you,' she said coldly.

Mrs McEvoy looked startled. 'Your husband? Why, I thought he was the children's Grandfa ....'

Her husband nudged her quickly. 'Has he joined Weight Watchers yet?' he put in hurriedly, eager to cover up his wife's mistake.

'Whatever for?' asked our bewildered Mother. Father had an athlete's figure, and I mean an athlete like Kenny Dalglish and not Jeff Capes.

'He seemed quite keen to lose some weight when he showed us round,' said Mrs McEvoy lamely. 'I told him all about how I lost 20 pounds with them and we already have an elderly person with our group.'

Mother was completely lost by now. She opened the front door as wide as she could and held out her hand formally.

'Goodbye, Mrs McEvoy, nice to have met you, Goodbye. Mr McEvoy.' The McEvoys shook hands and hurried away.

Mother stared after them before she shut the door and then turned to stare at us.

'Elderly gentleman? Lose weight? Your Father must have been play acting.'

Father denied all previous knowledge of the McEvoys when he came down to put his signature alongside Mother's on the contract documents. Steve and I expected this, we knew who had shown them round the house.

A mayor of Frome was shown round an old house in the town by a lady who, according to the neighbours, had been dead for years. And I was present when the old chair was solemnly inspected by a little girl who said thoughtfully, 'I can see an old fat man sitting in that chair. But I know he isn't really there.'

CURIOUS WILTSHIRE

Mary Delorme

Photographs by Duncan Skene

In this original and substantial work, historian and author Mary Delorme presents in-depth studies of six features of Wiltshire which contribute much to the uniqueness of the county: Water Meadows, White Horses, Sarsen Stones, Dew Ponds, Blind Houses and Tithe Barns.

The well researched and expertly written text is complemented by some 60 specially commissioned black and white photographs which illustrate aspects of *Curious Wiltshire* visible today.

229x145mm   160 pages   Full colour cover   ISBN 0 948578 00 9   Price £4.95

MENDIP RAMBLES

Peter Wright

Illustrations by Julia Manning

The twelve circular rambles described in this book, of around 5 miles each, guide th walker about a region of hill country which is a lesser known face of the green and pleasa. land of Somerset.

The highest point is reached on Blackdown at over a thousand feet. Between this ar the Somerset levels are windswept hillsides, spectacular inland cliffs, jungly combe caverns and swallets and magnificent sweeping views.

Peter Wright lives in Somerset and gains much of his livelihood on the Mendips as we as walking there whenever he can. His keen sense of history, curiosity about all observes and his understanding and sympathy with the natural world engages the read and rambler throughout.

198x128mm   96 pages   Full colour cover   12 pen and ink drawings
13 maps   ISBN 0 950653 7 2   Price £2.95

The above books may be obtained from your local bookshop or from the publisher, pos free, at 1 The Shambles, Bradford on Avon, Wiltshire.